C000005490

Nukenomics

The commercialisation of Britain's nuclear industry

Ian Jackson

With a Foreword by The Rt. Hon. The Lord Jenkin of Roding

Special

NUCLEAR ENGINEERING
INTERNATIONAL

Publications

Nuclear Engineering International Special Publications

All rights reserved. No part of this publication may be reproduced or transmitted in any form or by any means, including photocopying and recording, without the written permission of the copyright holder, application for which should be addressed to the Publishers. Such written permission must also be obtained before any part of this publication is stored in a retrieval system of any nature.

ISBN 978-1-903077-55-9

© 2008 Progressive Media Markets Ltd

Typesetting by Karen Townsend
Cover design by Natalie Kyne
Artwork for graphs by Shehnaz Jackson
Cover image by iStockphoto
Printed and bound by Formara Limited, 16 The Candlemakers,
Temple Farm Industrial Estate, Southend-on-Sea, Essex SS2 5RX, United Kingdom

Nuclear Engineering International Special Publications, Progressive House,
2 Maidstone Road, Foots Cray, Sidcup, Kent DA14 5HZ, United Kingdom
www.neimagazine.com

About the Author

Ian Jackson joined the British nuclear industry in 1986 working initially at the Atomic Energy Research Establishment (AERE) Harwell then later as a nuclear regulator. He is the author of *Siting New Nuclear Power Stations: Availability and Options for Government* published alongside the 2007 Energy White Paper. He received the Environment Agency's plain language award in 1999 for his report on the regulation of atomic weapons sites and has advised many public and private sector organisations on nuclear issues, including: AEA Technology, AMEC-NNC, AIM Investments, Bain & Company, Bear Stearns & Company, Belgonucleaire, Bridgepoint Capital, British Nuclear Fuels (BNFL), the Committee on Radioactive Waste Management (CoRWM), the Department of Trade and Industry (DTI), the Department for Environment, Food and Rural Affairs (Defra), the Environment Agency, EnergySolutions, Fleet Support Limited, Halcrow, Hunting-BRAE, NIREX, Nitron, the Ohio Public Employees Retirement System (OPERS), the Organisation for Economic Co-operation and Development (OECD), RWE npower, Shaw Group, Westinghouse and the United Kingdom Atomic Energy Authority (UKAEA). He is a member of the Society for Radiological Protection (SRP) and the British Nuclear Energy Society (BNES). Married with three school-age children, Ian Jackson lives near Warrington in the UK.

For Shehnaz, Yasmin, Zack and Nash

and in memory of my father David John Jackson, 1940-2006,
who taught me a great deal about how the world really works

Contents

Chapter 4

Selling Plutonium: The Market for MOX

Chapter 5

Beyond Carbon: Nuclear Reactor Economics

Figures

Foreword

Last year, the Institute of Economic Affairs published a very salutary monograph entitled *They Meant Well: Government Project Disasters*. This was a history of six major 20th Century public sector projects which all led to enormous waste of taxpayers' money. They ranged from the R.101 Airship (1922-30) to the Millennium Dome (1995-2000). Chapter 4 of this immensely readable analysis dealt with nuclear power (1958-78). The programme led to huge losses which had to be picked up by taxpayers. The author, Professor D R Myddelton, summed up the principal causes of this disastrous experience as "three interacting state monopolies, supported by an interventionist state."

I believe that the lessons from this experience have been learned, but it has taken a long time and there is certainly further to go. In the 21st Century, with Britain facing steeply rising fossil fuel energy costs, a growing dependence on foreign gas and oil from unstable sources, and a compelling need to move to a low carbon economy, the UK Government has been forced to announce a programme of building new nuclear power stations, both in order to achieve greater security of supply and as a major contribution to fighting climate change.

However, in place of the state-owned and state-run electricity generating industry that dominated the scene up until the early 1990s, Ministers in successive Governments have recognised that competitive markets are far more likely to provide efficient and effective methods of providing energy supplies. In the 1990s, almost all the electricity generating companies were transferred to the private sector. In 2004, the Nuclear Decommissioning Authority was set up and is obliged by Statute to put out to competitive tender contracts for the decommissioning of nuclear reactors that have reached the end of their lives. Most recently, the January 2008 *White Paper on Nuclear Power* committed the Government to encouraging private sector industry to investing the huge sums needed to build the next generation of nuclear power stations and to upgrade the transmission and distribution networks needed to bring supplies to consumers.

Further, both major political parties have made it clear that this must be done without public subsidy. In particular, the Energy Bill seeks to put in place a watertight regime for ensuring that back end costs (*i.e.* decommissioning and waste disposal) are fully borne by the companies investing in new build; and the costs of decommissioning and dealing with legacy waste are being identified and the taxpayers' liability for this, which is enormous, is being quantified. The hope is that the massive mistakes in the earlier programmes, graphically described by Professor Myddelton, will be avoided; that the new programme launched in the very different world energy climate of the 21st Century, will be wholly privately financed; and that the construction, operation, decommissioning and the disposal of waste will be undertaken by private sector companies under various forms of competitive enterprise. The Government's role is intended to be limited to regulation, including the all-important safety regulation at all stages, and managing the contracts with the private sector engineering companies who will be charged with the task of decommissioning and dealing with nuclear waste.

But this process starts with major handicaps. The British nuclear industry has been progressively dismantled and run down over recent decades; research and development spending has been massively cut back; the skilled workforce at all levels has been run down, with fewer and fewer new recruits joining. Even worse, where the UK had substantial nuclear assets, many of them have been sold off to overseas buyers so that the new UK programme is bound to be heavily dependent on foreign expertise and engineering capacity. It is being widely said that the biggest waste has been the waste of time in reaching decisions so that starting to rebuild our nuclear capacity has been seriously delayed.

Yet, the compelling logic of the energy and environment situation in which Britain finds herself means that immensely strenuous efforts will now have to be made on all sides if the industry is to deliver the new nuclear build programme within the timescales required "to keep the lights on". For a Government which only six years ago apparently believed that there might be no need for any new nuclear build, opting instead for "keeping the nuclear option open", now to be talking, as the Secretary of State for Business, Enterprise & Regulatory Reform did recently, of the need to press ahead "urgently" with the new build programme, is a near 180 degree turn – but five or even ten years too late. Other countries are ahead of us in the queue for major items of equipment, such as reactor vessels, where there are very few firms in the world able to supply. The programmes to train more nuclear engineers and scientists are just beginning to get underway in the universities and institutes; and the decisions needed to restart a meaningful research effort have been endlessly delayed.

A great deal has been talked and written about all this, and against the background of a population that had become very sceptical, even hostile, about the wisdom and benefits of building new nuclear power stations, it has been difficult to find well-informed and unprejudiced sources of detailed factual information about the economics of nuclear power that will determine how the future of the industry will develop.

Readers of Ian Jackson's excellent book, *Nukenomics*, will gain a very deep insight into the economics of the nuclear industry as it was in the past, as it is now, and is likely to be in the decades ahead. It is very well written in an admirably clear style which involves as little technical jargon as possible in what is inevitably a very technical subject. It could serve as a useful introduction to the study of the subject by a layman coming new to it. But at the same time, it could also be of great value to those who are directly involved in the decisions of the Government and of the industries concerned with nuclear power. I can commend it without reservation.

Patrick Jenkin
The Rt. Hon. The Lord Jenkin of Roding

Biographical Note

Lord Jenkin is a Conservative Peer. He served as Chief Secretary to the Treasury and Energy Minister in Prime Minister Edward Heath's Government and as Secretary of State for Social Services, Secretary of State for Industry and Secretary of State for the Environment in Prime Minister Margaret Thatcher's Government.

Preface

Nukenomics developed from a series of business-level articles that I wrote for *Nuclear Engineering International* magazine looking at the private sector nuclear market emerging in Britain. Once an industry run mainly by scientists and engineers, the nuclear sector has been substantially commercialised by the British government, introducing a much stronger business culture to nuclear operations. *Nukenomics* was written to help generalist readers understand the major trends and market forces that are actively shaping the future development of the nuclear industry today, by explaining not just what things are happening but, more fundamentally, why.

Following the birth of atomic energy at the end of the Second World War, the British nuclear industry grew swiftly under state control, reaching a peak of industrial activity and technological maturity by the mid 1970s. Then everything changed. A combination of high interest rates, over-supply of electricity capacity, cheaper availability of oil and natural gas, and public fears following the Chernobyl and Three Mile Island nuclear accidents abruptly ended most nuclear power station development projects, not just in Britain but also across much of Western Europe and North America.

Now, after a period of relative stagnation over the past two decades, the British nuclear industry is once again experiencing rapid and turbulent commercial change, transforming from a handful of public sector owned organisations into a series of private sector ones ready to tackle Britain's £100-billion-plus nuclear clean-up legacy. The impact of this change has been profound. An entire industry has been restructured. The old state-owned giants British Nuclear Fuels, Magnox Electric and the United Kingdom Atomic Energy Authority have been virtually swept aside, replaced by the Nuclear Decommissioning Authority – a new stream-lined organisation that thinks and acts more like a financial regulator than a nuclear agency.

At the same time, just when the future of nuclear energy looked set to be in terminal decline, the politics of global warming have delivered a dramatic return to respectability for nuclear power. As the threat of climate change from man-made carbon emissions appears to be accelerating towards a global tipping point, significant investment in new British nuclear power stations now seems certain; a situation that was unthinkable just a few years ago.

Nukenomics explores the dynamics of this newly revitalised nuclear market by looking at five major commercial themes addressing key business questions.

- Chapter 1, *Paying for Nuclear Clean-up: The Decommissioning Market*, explains why nuclear decommissioning costs paid for by British taxpayers are skyrocketing and how the government is attempting to bring these costs under control through privatisation of the nuclear industry. After examining the underlying factors responsible for driving an explosion in nuclear decommissioning costs, Chapter 1 analyses the market opportunity for nuclear clean-up firms and the scale of the financial risks and rewards available to market investors. The chapter explains the strategic dilemmas and paradoxes intrinsic within the restructured nuclear market and how private sector companies can best position themselves to exploit the commercial opportunities presented.
- Chapter 2, *Sites for Sale: Selling Nuclear Real Estate*, looks at the government's future ambitions for selling cleaned up nuclear sites to commercial property developers and energy utility companies. After examining the financial effects of radioactive contamination

on property prices, and the attitude of major banks and lenders funding investment, Chapter 2 discusses the potential ranges of valuations of sites for new nuclear reactor build projects, and the differing sales and bidding strategies that might realistically be adopted by the government and competing energy utility companies.

- Chapter 3, *Pricing Waste: The Economics of Nuclear Repositories*, examines the search for a final dump site for Britain's historic nuclear waste legacy and the likely cost implications for taxpayers. After several failed attempts at finding a disposal location the government is now offering to negotiate financial incentives with local communities to accept the waste. Chapter 3 discusses possible bidding strategies that could be adopted by communities competing to host a repository, how much money they should ask for in compensation and why. Chapter 3 also looks at the thorny question of how much cash energy utility companies might be asked to pay for disposing of extra wastes from new nuclear power station build, which is likely to triple the total radioactivity in the community's repository. The chapter looks at some alternative storage solutions if negotiations break down or if no host community actually comes forward.

- Chapter 4, *Selling Plutonium: The Market for MOX*, examines Britain's role in the supply of uranium-plutonium mixed oxide (MOX) nuclear fuel manufactured from foreign plutonium stored at Sellafield. The chapter looks at the financing of the Sellafield MOX Plant (SMP), intended by the government to be a profitable commercial venture, and forecasts that taxpayers stand to lose several billion pounds. Chapter 4 goes on to examine the government's options for dealing with Britain's own much larger stockpile of plutonium regarded by the nuclear industry as a valuable energy resource. Despite a MOX market crash in 2006 the chapter discusses the re-emergence of the MOX business as a route for destroying stockpiles of surplus plutonium as part of a non-commercial disposition strategy.

- Chapter 5, *Beyond Carbon: Nuclear Reactor Economics*, discusses nuclear power's dramatic return to respectability as a low-carbon energy source to help combat climate change. The chapter looks at the economic justification for building a new generation of nuclear power stations, and how the fortunes of nuclear energy are crucially geared towards the carbon market developing in Europe. The chapter discusses the critical factors affecting nuclear energy investment and how nuclear power plants might make a decent profit for investors if carbon prices remain high over the long term.

All financial and technical data used in *Nukenomics* are derived from publicly available reports believed to be the most up-to-date official information sources as of early April 2008. Calculations were performed using a Hewlett Packard HP12C financial calculator and an HP42S scientific calculator. For simplicity, cost estimates are undiscounted in present day 2008 prices, except for some historic cost estimates and pricing information where the original price and year is used instead.

Nukenomics is based on my business experience as a consultant to the nuclear industry over the past five years. But the usefulness of any business book ultimately depends on the quality of the background research underpinning it. In this regard I am especially grateful to Stephen Tarlton at *Nuclear Engineering International* magazine, Rob Edwards at *New Scientist* magazine, Nick Sloan at the National Audit Office, Judith Hollands at the Nuclear Decommissioning Authority, Dorothy Seed at British Nuclear Fuels, Steve Mansfield at the

CoRWM Secretariat and Jean McSorley at Greenpeace who all very kindly shared with me various internal governmental reports released under the Freedom of Information Act 2000. These reports, whilst technically speaking are all freely available to the public, are actually very hard to find in practice without guidance from expert colleagues pointing my research in the right direction, and occasionally offering gentle course-corrections when necessary. I am also grateful to John Large at Large & Associates for technical advice on many practical aspects of nuclear reactor physics. I am deeply indebted to The Right Honourable The Lord Jenkin of Roding who injected a number of wider political insights and real-word perspectives into my consulting work, that have proved extremely helpful in framing the thinking behind *Nukenomics*. Finally, I would like to thank my publisher Stephen Tarlton at *Nuclear Engineering International* magazine, who both gave me the opportunity and encouragement to publish *Nukenomics*, and also greatly improved its readability through his impressive editing skills and knowledge of the nuclear industry. Any errors or omissions in this book remain my responsibility, as do the interpretations and opinions expressed.

Ian Jackson
Warrington, UK
April 2008

Chapter 1

Paying for Nuclear Clean-up: The Decommissioning Market

Regime change

The small 19th Century village of Moor Row situated in the northwest of England some 318 miles from London, is not one of the places that you usually think of as a major financial centre responsible for managing a £73 billion government investment programme spread over the next 120 years. But Moor Row is home to Britain's Nuclear Decommissioning Authority, a government-funded agency that spends some £2.5 billion of taxpayers money each year, enough to add a penny to the basic rate of UK income tax, on the hazardous business of dismantling shutdown nuclear reactors and old nuclear research plants. The total will almost certainly be higher since the £73 billion estimate excludes the estimated £9.7 billion cost of decommissioning military nuclear weapons plants and nuclear powered submarines, potentially a further £8.6 billion for decommissioning commercial nuclear power stations that are due to retire over the next 15 years, and at least £10 billion for an underground disposal facility for higher-level radioactive waste. The final nuclear bill for the taxpayer is likely to be closer to £101 billion, about the same cost as running Britain's National Health Service for a year. And there is every prospect that it will continue to rise. Over the past five years official estimates of nuclear clean-up costs have escalated on average by around nine per cent each year, growing from £48 billion in 2002 to £73 billion by 2007. These estimates jumped 16 per cent in 2007 alone and have grown four times faster than Britain's average two per cent annual inflation level over the same five-year period.

As a direct result of this exponential growth in nuclear costs, and the government's efforts to slow them down, the nuclear industry is now experiencing rapid and turbulent commercial change, transforming from a handful of public sector owned organisations into a series of private sector ones instead. The impact of this much-needed change has been profound. An entire industry has been restructured. The old state-owned giants British Nuclear Fuels plc (BNFL), Magnox Electric and the United Kingdom Atomic Energy Authority (UKAEA) have been virtually swept aside, replaced by the Nuclear Decommissioning Authority – a new streamlined organisation that thinks and acts more like a financial regulator than a nuclear agency.

The nuclear industry's past approach to cleaning up retired British nuclear plants in the 1980s and 1990s was to defer decommissioning, putting off the fateful day until as far as possible into the future. The financial justification was explained in the 1995 White Paper, *Review of Radioactive Waste Management Policy – Final Conclusions*, which more or less allowed operators to defer reactor decommissioning for up to 100 years, provided that they set up a pension fund to deal with the nuclear waste. All this changed in 2002 when Prime Minister Tony Blair's 'New Labour' government began revolutionising the way in which nuclear clean-up is funded and managed.

For much of its 60-year history, the nuclear industry in Britain has operated as a large nationalised monopoly staffed by civil servants working in the public sector. What makes this revolution particularly interesting is that by the end of the decade almost all of the nuclear clean-up work will be undertaken not by small armies of public sector workers but by commercial firms competing against each other in the private sector with the ambition of improving efficiency and reducing the multi-billion pound clean-up bill that must eventually be paid for by future generations of British taxpayers. The strategy is ingenious. The government couldn't sell its nuclear liabilities as it had attempted to do with the British Energy privatisation during the 1990s, so it contractorised them instead. Over the next few years the plan is to create an instant mini-market of experienced commercial organisations ready and willing to compete for some £73 billion of nuclear decommissioning contracts, around half of which will be spent during the next two decades.

The Blair government's nuclear clean-up revolution began in July 2000, when the Department of Trade and Industry (DTI) began a five-yearly periodic quinquennial review of the UKAEA, which today is responsible for around eight per cent of the government's total clean-up bill for civil nuclear energy. The review team examined the commercial success of the UKAEA's Decommissioning and Radioactive Waste Management Operations (DRAW-MOPS) nuclear decommissioning programme that had begun ten years earlier in 1991 after government funding for the Authority's nuclear energy research functions had ended.

In 1994 the UKAEA created a commercial division called AEA Technology, which was subsequently privatised in 1996. The proportion of nuclear decommissioning work undertaken by commercial contractors to the slimmed-down UKAEA steadily increased from 24 per cent in 1994 to 60 per cent by 1997 and reached a peak of 83 per cent by 2000. The Authority found that by using commercial firms bidding to carry out decommissioning work under competitive tendering in the 1990s, the Authority had made cost savings from 20 to 30 per cent between the price at which a competitive tender was actually let by the Authority and the average tender price.

Faced with a spiralling bill for nuclear decommissioning, the prospect of up to 30 per cent cost savings proved highly attractive to government civil servants. In November 2001 the DTI's Quinquennial Review team published its final report, which in essence recommended that the government should introduce commercial competition across all of the government's civil nuclear liabilities portfolio – at that time estimated to be around £48 billion. At the same time, the board of the much larger BNFL announced that its long-term nuclear decommissioning liabilities exceeded its assets, in effect making the state-owned company technically bankrupt. Although BNFL actually had strong cashflow from spent fuel reprocessing income and electricity generation income, its longer-term liabilities position was bleak. The company announced a pre-tax loss of £2.3 billion in 2002 and later shelved its ambitions for a possible flotation on the stock market.

Viewed in retrospect, the Quinquennial Review of the UKAEA was a key milestone and was the first serious effort to put a total price on the UK's entire nuclear clean-up bill. On 28th November 2001, Secretary of State for Trade and Industry Patricia Hewitt announced the government's plan to restructure the civil nuclear industry, which was subsequently formalised in the July 2002 White Paper *Managing the Nuclear Legacy: A Strategy for Action*. Hence, what initially had begun as an administrative review of the running of the slimmed-down UKAEA after its partial privatisation, became the trigger for a major restructuring of the entire civil nuclear industry encompassing all of the government-owned civil nuclear assets of the UKAEA and BNFL, and the Magnox Electric nuclear power station fleet.

The major change under the Nuclear Decommissioning Authority is a shift away from vertically integrated site management where a public sector company both operates a nuclear licensed site and provides its own support services, to a new contract-based system in which a management contractor will manage decommissioning activities on behalf of the Nuclear Decommissioning Authority, aided by the resident site workforce and support services from the private sector.

Nuclear prisoners

Nuclear energy is a climate-friendly electricity generation technology that offers utility companies and energy consumers large amounts of reliable baseload power with very low carbon emissions. But choosing nuclear has long-term implications. Perhaps more than any other technology, nuclear power has the habit of making any government the prisoner of past decisions. The economic impact of nuclear energy decisions made in the 1950s and 1960s are still being felt by taxpayers today.

Investing in nuclear technology uniquely captures governments in a lengthy cycle of expenditure that once started, will take a century to exit – 10 years to license and build a modern nuclear power station, 60 years to operate and maintain it, and 30 years to decommission it. Few other technologies have the capacity to bind government spending for a 100 years. As a result, the long-term costs of nuclear power can only really be estimated and estimates are only as good as the economic assumptions on which they are based. For example, nuclear power stations are expensive to build and so must be financed by bank loans from the private sector, making the total cost of construction very sensitive to fluctuations in interest rates. But national inflation and interest rates can vary tremendously over the century lifecycle of a nuclear power station. Investing in nuclear energy has been likened to a 60-year gamble on interest rates.

The Office of National Statistics 2004 report *Consumer Price Inflation Since 1750* points out that since the beginning of the Second World War, consumer prices have increased more than 40-fold over the past 70 years. Partly because of this inflationary pressure, accurately forecasting the total cost of front end nuclear build and back end nuclear clean-up still remains more of an art than a science.

Energy investors generally remain wary about dealing with the back end liability costs of decommissioning and nuclear waste disposal unless these costs can be fixed in some way by government price guarantees. Moreover, nuclear costs are notoriously hard to control in an industry where safety is at stake and must remain paramount, irrespective of economic arguments.

Whatever the future of nuclear power in the energy supply market, there remains a considerable £101 billion legacy of historic nuclear plant and radioactive contamination that must now be decommissioned and cleaned up. This work will be carried out by private industry working on behalf of the government and paid for by taxpayers. Companies and their investors entering the nuclear decommissioning services market must bear in mind that the economics of nuclear clean-up are relatively new. Historical commercial lessons learned from private sector involvement in nuclear power station build during the 1960s and 1970s may not necessarily apply to present-day nuclear clean-up. The true costs of nuclear decommissioning were probably not fully appreciated until the beginning of the 1990s, in the final days of Prime Minister Margaret Thatcher's Conservative government when the financial markets first had to put a value on the proposed privatisation of nuclear power stations.

To understand why Britain has apparently sleep-walked into a £101 billion mountain of nuclear debt requires a brief history lesson, starting with the atomic bomb.

Labour's atom bomb

Britain's nuclear industry was born 60 years ago, almost immediately after the end of the Second World War. Two months after the United States of America dropped the first atomic bomb on Hiroshima and then a second bomb on Nagasaki, Labour Prime Minister Clement Attlee announced on 29th October 1945 that Britain was to set up its own research establishment to study all aspects of atomic energy, with the intention of developing a British atomic weapon. The site chosen for what was to become Britain's first nuclear establishment was a former RAF military airfield located near the village of Harwell in Oxfordshire, about 56 miles west of London. In January 1946 Harwell became home to the Atomic Energy Research Establishment and a £53 million per year government-funded nuclear construction programme began, equivalent to spending about £1.6 billion in today's money.

Upon his re-election as Conservative Prime Minister in 1951, Winston Churchill is said to have been astonished that the Attlee government had managed to spend almost £100 million on the nuclear programme without informing Parliament. In Britain's fragile post-war economy £100 million was a staggering sum of public money, reflecting the importance that the government placed on developing its own nuclear weapons technology. Even so, this was still far less than the $2 billion America had spent during the war to develop the first two atomic bombs.

Unfortunately for Britain, in August 1946 the US Congress passed the McMahon Act, which prevented America sharing its newly acquired nuclear technology with other countries including its British allies – a situation that was only relaxed 12 years later when the United States agreed to share nuclear technology with Britain under the 1958 US-UK Mutual Defence Agreement signed by President Eisenhower.

Nevertheless, despite this temporary political setback in US relations, the independent British atomic programme made rapid progress working alone and by August 1947, just 20 months after Harwell officially opened, *TIME* magazine reported that Britain's first atomic pile, a prototype nuclear reactor called GLEEP (Graphite Low Energy Experimental Pile), had begun operating at Harwell. Britain subsequently detonated its first atomic bomb, *Hurricane*, in the Montebello islands on 3rd October 1952, prompting the American government to offer Dr William Penney, the 43-year-old head of Britain's weapon programme, four times his reported $8,000 salary to join the US atomic programme instead. Dr Penney declined, apparently preferring British thanks to American cash. Later in 1953, *Blue Danube*, a low yield 20 kiloton nuclear weapon, came into military service deployed on Royal Air Force bombers. *Blue Danube* may only have been a small weapon but it achieved the key political objective of making Britain a nuclear-armed military power.

From what limited information is known of the United Kingdom Atomic Energy Authority's (UKAEA's) early Parliamentary funding, the cost of developing Britain's nuclear weapons capability from Harwell's birth in 1946 through to the successful *Hurricane* test in 1952 was probably around £350 million, equivalent to £7.5 billion today. But of course this initial cost was just the tip of the iceberg. Simply owning a nuclear weapon is of little military value to a state without also having the defensive capability to successfully deploy and deliver it against a real military target. The nuclear infrastructure necessary to maintain Britain's national nuclear deterrent from the early 1950s through to the present day necessarily included an expensive mixture of long range bombing aircraft, submarines, ballistic missiles and their associated airfield and dockyard maintenance facilities, as well nuclear reactors to produce plutonium and tritium raw materials needed for warhead components and factories to manufacture, assemble and service the atomic weapons.

Faced with the military imperative of the Cold War, the back end tasks of nuclear decommissioning and environmental clean-up of redundant nuclear plants understandably took something of a back seat. Little, if any, nuclear decommissioning of military facilities was done on a serious scale until the mid 1990s. Not surprisingly, the accumulated legacy of military nuclear clean-up work that remains to be carried out has been estimated by the Ministry of Defence to be worth some £9.8 billion as of July 2006.

Calder Hall, the world's first nuclear power station

Following the success of the first British atomic weapon test and the introduction of *Blue Danube*, serious political attention began to be focused on the possibility of generating electricity from nuclear power. Because Britain's post-war economy still remained vulnerable to relatively expensive supplies of coal and oil, the prospect of apparently limitless power from atomic energy was very attractive to politicians, who were perhaps captivated by the awesome psychological imagery of atomic explosions. The early nuclear pioneers however faced a daunting task. While atomic bombs could be engineered without too much regard for what happened to their internal components after the bomb successfully detonated, nuclear reactors were a much more difficult proposition because they needed to operate safely and reliably for many years.

Before nuclear power stations could be built, scientists first needed to understand how their construction materials might behave – or misbehave – when bombarded for an expected 10 to 20 years by the extremely intense levels of radiation found inside the graphite core of a working reactor. Would the core's construction materials remain strong indefinitely or would they weaken? Would they age and degrade more quickly? Would they become brittle and fracture? Would they bend or warp? How long could they safely contain their highly radioactive fuel? Moreover, the heat-producing nuclear reactions taking place deep inside the uranium fuelled core of the reactor created fission products and activation products – highly radioactive versions of ordinary chemical elements – as well as entirely new transuranic radioactive substances that had not previously existed on Earth, whose properties were mostly unknown and their health effects uncertain. Nevertheless, despite these appreciable knowledge gaps, British nuclear scientists made swift progress and on 17th October 1956 Her Majesty Queen Elizabeth II opened the world's first civil nuclear power station, Calder Hall, in Cumbria, northwest England. *TIME* magazine's article *First Nuclear Power* described Calder Hall as a technical triumph for Britain, first to achieve atomic power on a serious scale

– each of Calder Hall's four reactors had a 50 megawatt (MWe) net capacity that helped solve a fuel shortage for the country's industry. This was indeed a tremendous achievement for Britain's nuclear programme that had started virtually from scratch only 10 years earlier.

Arguably, the rapid progress made in developing nuclear power was helped by less stringent attention to nuclear safety than would be required today. In the prevailing deferential social culture of the 1950s in which the public generally accepted authority and official thinking, the risks from atomic energy were regarded as technical issues best left for scientists rather than politicians to manage – something that politicians perhaps later came to regret after the world's second-worst nuclear accident occurred at Britain's Windscale works on 10th October 1957 when a military nuclear reactor caught fire. Nuclear safety and environmental protection legislation was introduced in the aftermath of the fire, bringing a welcome degree of independent regulatory oversight to nuclear activities for the first time, in part reflecting the more questioning social attitudes and culture of the 1960s. However during the 1940s and 1950s definitive answers to nuclear safety questions were not easily available to politicians. The regulation of nuclear safety was mostly carried out in-house by the United Kingdom Atomic Energy Authority's own internal safety branch. Like most truly leading-edge science, the development of Calder Hall required a virtually unique regulatory approach, in effect relying on staged operating experience to demonstrate that if the reactor worked, then it must be safe after all. This is somewhat in contrast to the modern day 'precautionary principle' that applies before the introduction of any new technology, which must first be proved to be reasonably safe before widespread commercial adoption.

Magnox power stations

Calder Hall was not just a technical triumph but a practical demonstration that it was economically feasible to generate large amounts of electricity from nuclear power. Britain's first generation of nuclear reactors were named after the type of fuel used in the Calder Hall reactor in which uranium was clad in a special non-oxidising magnesium alloy called Magnox. The economic case was set out in the government's 1955 White Paper *A Programme of Nuclear Power*, which envisaged building a series of Magnox nuclear power stations based on the Calder Hall design, to provide an installed capacity of 1,500 to 2,000 megawatts (MWe) satisfying 25 per cent of Britain's electricity needs at a total cost of £300 million. With the benefit of hindsight the £300 million estimate, worth £5.7 billion today, proved to be optimistic. In the Nuclear Decommissioning Authority's five-year strategy published in March 2006, the future clean-up bill for the Magnox decommissioning programme alone was estimated to be £12 billion, excluding the already sunk costs of building and operating the Magnox fleet over the past 50 years.

The feasibility of the Magnox programme did not mean that nuclear power was commercially competitive with coal-fired power stations in 1955. In any case the electricity supply industry in Britain was nationalised with no real commercial competition between different forms of electricity generation. Nevertheless, although the Magnox programme was probably not economically competitive with coal, it was at least affordable. The economic assumptions of the 1955 White Paper were a capital cost of between £10 million to £20 million for each Magnox nuclear power station, an installed capacity of 100-150 MWe, an expected plant lifetime of between 10 to 20 years and uranium fuel costs of £5 million recurring every three to five years. The Suez oil crisis in 1956 further increased the political enthusiasm for nuclear power and led to a doubling of the Magnox programme. Magnox power stations were eventually built at 11 sites across Britain, with each station containing a pair of twin reactors of around 400 MWe (2 x 200 MWe) capacity. The only exceptions were Calder Hall and Chapelcross which both had four smaller Magnox reactors (4 x 50 MWe). The last one to be built, at Wylfa in Wales, opened in 1971 with a net capacity of 980 MWe (2 x 490 MWe). Wylfa is officially scheduled to close by 2010 although its operating lifetime could perhaps be extended to 2014, the most likely closure date when the station's operating licence becomes due for a major 10-year periodic safety review by the nuclear regulators.

A fact not widely appreciated is that the 1957 Windscale fire had a significant but belated impact on the economics of the Magnox programme during the 1960s. The fire occurred in the graphite core of a military reactor that had overheated as a result of an uncontrolled Wigner energy release. Follow-up research on the behaviour of graphite led to the introduction of small amounts of methane into the carbon dioxide gas coolant used in Magnox reactors. In the aftermath of the Windscale fire, research and development work to understand the Wigner energy instability also revealed that at the higher operating temperatures required for Magnox reactors, the graphite core suffered accelerated weight loss from radiolysis, reducing its strength and neutron moderation capability in the longer term. Radiolysis was slowed by the deliberate introduction of trace amounts of methane into the carbon dioxide gas coolant.

The methane was intended to help reduce the radiation-induced damage to the reactors' graphite core, but unfortunately the methane itself had the unexpected side-effect of corroding the restraining steelwork in the core. The corrosion problem was potentially so serious that the capacity of the Magnox fleet had to be derated by 20 per cent because the weakened reactor structure needed to be run at lower operating temperatures for safety reasons. For Wylfa, the last of the Magnox stations designed and built in the 1960s before the steel corrosion problem had been established, the option was to either derate each of the twin reactors from 600 MWe down to 490 MWe to inhibit steel corrosion or to dismantle the reactor and replace all of the susceptible steelwork. The derating option was chosen at great detriment to the station's operational efficiency and economics over its lifetime.

AGR power stations

As the industrial manufacturing economy continued to expand in Britain in the early 1960s, the government began to consider the need for a second generation of new and more powerful nuclear power stations. The Magnox reactors were partially military in origin (Calder Hall was a dual use reactor capable of producing military grade plutonium as well as nuclear electricity). But as the nuclear power programme grew, becoming independent of the military in the 1970s, it was increasingly expected to operate profitably on commercial principles.

The 1964 White Paper, *The Second Nuclear Power Programme*, began a commercial competition for submission of new reactor designs, and in 1965 the government selected the 600 MWe Advanced Gas-cooled Reactor (AGR) to be built in pairs. In addition to the 4,190 MWe of Magnox capacity, the second generation of nuclear reactors was to provide Britain with a further 8,380 MWe of AGR capacity. In the 1960s oil was in plentiful supply but by the early 1970s fears over oil supplies from the Middle East once again played a key role in promoting the fortunes of nuclear power when the OPEC oil embargo in 1973 triggered a sharp rise in oil prices worldwide. AGR nuclear power stations were built at seven sites across Britain. The outlook today is that over the next 15 years all of Britain's AGR commercial nuclear power stations are due to retire, losing around 8 gigawatts (GWe) of low carbon electricity generation capacity, around 16 per cent of the country's electricity supply. Only Sizewell B, an American-designed modern 1,200 MWe pressurised water reactor (PWR) that opened in 1995 in Suffolk, is expected to keep operating much beyond 2023.

It has been a major criticism of the AGR programme that no two stations were identical. As Sir Arthur Hawkins, Chairman of the Central Electricity Generating Board (CEGB), remarked: "The scientists never allowed their babies to grow up." This meant that the cost reductions expected to be gained from constructing a series of power stations based on a single standardised reactor design were lost. Following their construction in the 1970s and 1980s the AGR stations were later privatised by the government in 1996. But after a major fall in wholesale electricity prices the government was forced to underwrite responsibility for decommissioning the AGR stations following the near financial collapse of their privatised owner, British Energy, in September 2002.

Privatisation experiments

The 1990s became an important testing ground for nuclear economics when significant parts of the British nuclear sector were placed on a commercial footing, exposing the industry to the full cost control discipline of the private sector for the first time. The government conducted three major market experiments: the £2.1 billion privatisation of British Energy, involving the sale of the civil AGR nuclear power station fleet and Britain's newly-built PWR; the £228 million privatisation of AEA Technology, the commercial division of the United Kingdom Atomic Energy Authority (UKAEA); and the full contractorisation of the Ministry of Defence's Devonport nuclear submarine base and four atomic weapons establishments under government-owned contractor-operated (GOCO) turnkey management arrangements, where private sector contractors managed some military nuclear facilities on behalf of the Ministry of Defence.

These separate privatisations involved three distinct commercial strategies: the British Energy privatisation sold power station 'assets', while the AEA Technology privatisation sold 'people' and the Defence commercialisation sold management 'contracts'. It was this latter military contracting approach that later proved to be the best suited to the commercially risky nature of the nuclear decommissioning business and subsequently laid much of the foundation for the commercialisation strategy now being applied to the whole of Britain by the Nuclear Decommissioning Authority.

By the late 1980s the organisational structure of the civil nuclear industry in Britain had evolved and matured into three main public sector players: the UKAEA, which operated the research and experimental reactor sites at Dounreay, Harwell, Winfrith and Windscale; British Nuclear Fuels plc (BNFL), which operated the uranium enrichment site at Capenhurst, the nuclear fuel manufacturing site at Springfields, the spent fuel storage and reprocessing site at

Sellafield and the low-level nuclear waste burial site at Drigg; and the Central Electricity Generating Board (and its Scottish counterpart the South of Scotland Electricity Board) which operated the 11 Magnox and seven AGR nuclear power stations. The military also operated its own smaller nuclear sites, notably the atomic weapons manufacturing and assembly plants at Aldermaston, Burghfield and Cardiff, the nuclear submarine dockyards at Devonport, Barrow, Rosyth and Faslane, the submarine fuel manufacturing plant at Derby, the Naval test reactor near Dounreay and the officer training reactor at the Royal Naval College, Greenwich. Of these players, the Central Electricity Generating Board was by far the largest organisation with a portfolio of mainly coal and nuclear power stations worth around £32 billion in the late 1980s.

After winning the 1987 general election for a historic third time, Prime Minister Margaret Thatcher's Conservative government privatised the Central Electricity Generating Board to create an electricity supply market. The 1988 White Paper, *Privatising Electricity: The Government's Proposals for the Privatisation of the Electricity Supply Industry in England and Wales*, implemented Energy Minister Nigel Lawson's 1982 speech on *The Market for Energy* in which he rejected nationalised energy planning by central government in favour of a free market approach where government would specify the energy outcomes it wanted to achieve, and the energy markets would provide the cheapest means of delivery. As things turned out, gas fired power stations rather than coal or nuclear power stations proved to be the most economic choice for the newly privatised electricity utility companies who made a 'dash for gas', building several new gas fired power stations in the early 1990s.

The government's initial plan was that the Central Electricity Generating Board's coal and nuclear power stations would be offered for sale, but the financial markets became increasingly concerned about taking on responsibility for nuclear decommissioning costs. As a result the nuclear power stations were withdrawn from sale at the last moment and temporarily placed inside two new state-owned companies Nuclear Electric and Scottish Nuclear. It was probably not until the financial markets had to put a price on the nuclear stations that the full financial implications of their eventual decommissioning costs were explored.

After another White Paper, *The Prospects for Nuclear Power in the United Kingdom*, was published in 1995, the seven AGR stations and one PWR station were eventually privatised and floated on the stock market as British Energy in 1996 raising £2.1 billion for the government – less than the price of what it cost to build just one of them, the brand new £2.8 billion Sizewell B PWR station. This 'eight for the price of one' deal probably reflected just how anxious the government was to get rid of as much of the nuclear industry off its hands as quickly as possible. Not surprisingly the Magnox nuclear power stations, with their remaining lifespan of less than 10 years and much lower electricity output, could not be sold at any price and remained in the public sector as Magnox Electric under the reluctant ownership of BNFL, which was given responsibility for running them by the government. The transfer of the Magnox decommissioning liabilities would eventually precipitate the break-up of BNFL following the board's announcement in November 2001 that the company's long-term decommissioning liabilities exceeded its assets.

The British Energy flotation had been unpopular with the financial markets. Uniquely for a government privatisation, investors immediately lost money as shares initially went on sale on 15th July 1996 at 203p, falling five per cent to 192p on the first day of trading before creeping back up to 205p three months later, just above the flotation price. Despite these initial jitters, over the next two and half years the price of British Energy shares steadily increased to a high of 733p in January 1999, as the electricity output from the AGR nuclear power stations grew, operating costs fell from a 20 per cent cut in the workforce, and power prices remained high in the wholesale electricity market.

However the introduction of competition into the energy markets began to result in a fall in electricity prices between 1999 to 2002. This was good news for consumers but bad news for British Energy, which was stuck with high fixed costs and inflexible nuclear generating plants. Unlike gas-fired power stations whose power output can be quickly increased from standby levels to meet daily changes in electricity demand, the output from nuclear power stations cannot easily be raised or lowered rapidly. Instead nuclear plants are intended to run continuously for months on end, normally for up to two years at a time. These operating characteristics mean that nuclear is best suited to producing reliable baseload power – a basic workhorse that steadily produces the everyday levels of electricity generation needed by Britain almost continuously at any given time of the year – while gas is better at quickly generating the extra marginal power levels needed to supply the changing daily peaks and troughs in electricity demand. Unfortunately a power price fall occurred between 1999 to 2002 in which the energy markets priced nuclear baseload power cheaply while the marginal gas fired power needed to meet fluctuations in demand became much more profitable for generators. This change in the market hit British Energy very badly. The company began losing money as the cost of producing nuclear electricity became higher than the market price at which it could sell it. On 5th September 2002, just six years after privatisation, British Energy announced that it had run out of cash and approached the government for £450 million of emergency state aid funding.

Britain's largest electricity generator had effectively gone bust. The situation was desperately serious for Britain's national interests. Without cash the company couldn't trade, and would have to shut down its 9.5 GWe nuclear power station fleet that provided 20 per cent of Britain's electricity supply, potentially triggering a widespread electricity blackout of the UK's national grid. The government was forced to step in and implemented a complex financial restructuring that effectively renationalised British Energy back into majority public ownership. This included the government underwriting financial responsibility for £14 billion of decommissioning and spent fuel liabilities that it thought it had privatised in 1996. Just when the financial sector was becoming comfortable with private ownership of nuclear power stations, British Energy had failed and shareholders including many small investors lost virtually all of their money. As one disgruntled letter writer to *The Times* put it on 14th September 2005: "As someone who invested £1,000 in British Energy and received for my pains £1.75 back... the nuclear industry has got to come up with more convincing figures than these to get anybody to invest."

The restructuring of British Energy was completed in January 2005 and the company relisted on the London Stock Exchange, albeit now with the government holding 64 per cent of the shares. British Energy makes payments into a government-backed Nuclear Liabilities Fund – essentially a pension fund for reactor clean-up – and any future shortfall will be picked up by the taxpayer. The most recent estimate by the Department of Trade and Industry has put the future cost of decommissioning the AGR stations at around £8.6 billion in 2007 prices. This figure rises to a total of £14 billion if the liabilities for reprocessing, storing and disposing of their spent reactor fuel are also included along with the decommissioning costs.

In June 2007 the government sold a 25 per cent stake in British Energy raising £2.1 billion, ironically the same amount that it had raised during the original 1996 flotation. But this time the government did not sell its entire shareholding and retained a 39 per cent stake in the company for strategic reasons. The £2.1 billion generated from the second British Energy sale was paid into the Nuclear Liabilities Fund as a dowry to help offset decommissioning costs. But the losers have been many private shareholders who lost their investment and the future generations of taxpayers underwriting any shortfall in paying the £8.6 billion decommissioning bill.

The UKAEA's nuclear decommissioning programme began in earnest after 1991 when government funding for its research functions was ended by Conservative Prime Minister John Major. The Authority created a commercial division in 1994 called AEA Technology that was subsequently privatised and floated on the stock market for £228 million in 1996, the last privatisation before the Conservative government was defeated in the 1997 general election. Unlike the privatisation of British Energy, which involved a sale of physical nuclear power station assets, the AEA Technology privatisation was a relatively novel sale of nuclear 'know-how' comprising mainly of the former nuclear research staff of Harwell, Culham and Risley that proved somewhat tricky for the financial markets to value.

AEA Technology initially did rather well on the stock market. Shares went on sale on 26th September 1996 at 280p and rose to 323p on the first day of trading. By the end of its first financial year as a publicly traded company, AEA Technology shares had reached 474p in March 2007 and by March 1998 shares had increased another 56 per cent to 738p, outperforming the 21 per cent growth of the FTSE100 share price index of leading companies. But a series of profit warnings reduced AEA Technology's value for investors and by 2001, just five years after privatisation, the government's flagship nuclear research company had almost completely exited the nuclear business to focus on more promising opportunities in the rail and environment sectors. AEA Technology sold the bulk of its nuclear consulting interests to Serco Assurance in 2001, and later its nuclear engineering business to RWE Nukem and its nuclear science business to Nexia Solutions both in 2003.

Today AEA Technology is a well respected energy and environment consultancy business. AEA Technology's strategic exit from nuclear – essentially driven by what it regarded as poor nuclear growth prospects coupled with tightening profit margins – came as a genuine shock for the government. The profit-driven reality of AEA Technology's difficult transition to the private sector proved to be highly influential on the Department of Trade and Industry's Quinquennial Review team, who noted with some concern that private companies were deliberately leaving and choosing not to enter the nuclear industry. Radical action was called for and it eventually came in the form of the Nuclear Decommissioning Authority.

Rise of the Nuclear Decommissioning Authority

In the past, the nuclear services market in the UK was essentially a vertically integrated closed market in which three public sector organisations, British Nuclear Fuels plc (BNFL), Magnox Electric and the United Kingdom Atomic Energy Authority (UKAEA) undertook the majority of decontamination and decommissioning work on behalf of the government. The Energy Act 2004 broke this near monopoly position, by finally bringing together all of the civil

public sector decommissioning activities under the single financial umbrella of a new centralised government funded body, the Nuclear Decommissioning Authority. The Nuclear
Decommissioning Authority was given responsibility for managing all of the government's
financial portfolio of civil nuclear liabilities in April 2005. This £73 billion portfolio will most
likely be expanded to include another £8.6 billion of liabilities for decommissioning British
Energy's fleet of AGR nuclear power stations as these are retired over the next 15 years. Under
the financial restructuring of British Energy, the government has the option to acquire for £1
any station that British Energy plans to close in its own economic interest, either to prolong
their operation or to decommission them. The Nuclear Decommissioning Authority has been
given responsibility by government for reviewing and approving British Energy's decommissioning plans.

A key part of the new financial arrangements, which are in effect regulated by the Nuclear
Decommissioning Authority, is that decommissioning contracts will be awarded under open
competition to buy in the best available expertise. This is likely to include both European and
American nuclear services companies as well as the existing British delivery organisations. The
Nuclear Decommissioning Authority is a small streamlined organisation of around 200 people with backgrounds mainly in finance and project management, that thinks and acts more
like a financial regulator than a nuclear agency. The major difference between the former
public sector nationalised management of the nuclear industry, and the new private sector
management arrangements under the Nuclear Decommissioning Authority is the introduction of American style commercial management culture that is expected to bring significant
cost reductions for nuclear decommissioning.

The government favours US management approaches toward nuclear clean-up because of
the perceived success of the US Department of Energy's decommissioning programme, one
of the largest nuclear clean-up programmes in the world. The American firm Bechtel, a key
player in US nuclear clean-up, advised the government on the formation of the Nuclear
Decommissioning Authority and a small team of senior Bechtel staff were seconded into the
government's Liabilities Management Unit (the precursor organisation to the Nuclear
Decommissioning Authority) to help set it up. Unsurprisingly the Nuclear Decommissioning
Authority's management models closely resemble the American system, with some important
fine tuning for the British regulatory environment.

These management changes reflect a much broader shift in public policy away from
nationalised state controlled management, towards private sector management of state
assets such as toll roads, schools, hospitals, research bodies, and so on. The new arrangements, where companies manage government nuclear facilities but do not own them, were
first pioneered by the Ministry of Defence in the 1990s for the management of the Atomic
Weapons Establishment sites at Aldermaston and Burghfield and the nuclear submarine base
at Devonport.

The shift from government to private control brought about a number of changes in the
way that the nuclear safety and environmental regulators granted regulatory licences to operate nuclear sites. The regulators who previously had licensed the 'owners' of each nuclear site
explained that they would now grant the regulatory operating licence to the company in
charge of the day-to-day operation of nuclear plant and whose staff managed its normal
operation. Prospective nuclear licensees must submit a management prospectus to the
regulators showing sufficient supervision and oversight to demonstrate that its chain of

command and ability to control activities on the site have not been compromised. The nuclear safety regulators refer to this as maintaining an 'intelligent customer' capability and this is a key prerequisite for companies to hold a nuclear site licence in Britain.

The contracting model reflected in the Energy Act 2004 envisages private sector site management contractors competing to manage nuclear sites, with successful bidders taking ownership of a Site Licence Company for the duration of the contract. The Site Licence Company employs the site workforce and holds the regulatory licences necessary to operate the site. The Energy Act allows the Nuclear Decommissioning Authority to take back owner-ship of a Site Licence Company or transfer it to another winning contractor when the existing site management contract comes to an end. For the duration of the contract the Site Licence Company is legally owned by the managing contractor appointed by the Nuclear Decommissioning Authority.

The Nuclear Decommissioning Authority initially granted both BNFL and the UKAEA transi-tional site management contracts running from April 2005 when the Nuclear Decommissioning Authority first became operational. But this was intended to be a somewhat temporary arrangement. In 2007 the Nuclear Decommissioning Authority announced the formation of seven new Site Licence Companies to manage its portfolio of 20 nuclear sites. The Authority plans to hold commercial competitions for 17-year nuclear site management contracts, which will be re-competed at approximately five-year intervals. The intention is to transfer control of each Site Licence Company to the winning contractor in the private sector or more likely to a winning consortium of contractors called a Parent Body Organisation.

The Nuclear Decommissioning Authority is keen that different management contractors will join together to form consortia to operate nuclear sites, rather than have a single man-agement contractor. The business argument is that a consortium will bring a diverse range of management skills into play. British nuclear companies have reacted to this trend by seek-ing partners, especially with companies that have American clean-up experience. In June 2007, EnergySolutions, a $2 billion American firm, became the first private sector company to manage the clean-up of the Nuclear Decommissioning Authority's former Magnox power station sites.

The United States is a reasonable analogue for the UK nuclear decommissioning market and its scope for commercialisation. While experiences with US nuclear waste may not always be typical, they are important because America has the oldest nuclear programme in the world, the largest amount of waste needing disposition and the most financial resources to do so sensibly and safely. The US situation provides a best case analysis of typical waste relat-ed problems that could be encountered by the Nuclear Decommissioning Authority in Britain. Nevertheless, making progress has not been easy, even for the Americans. Soon after entering the White House, incoming US President George W Bush's administration ordered a root and branch review of the Department of Energy's $220 billion Environmental Management Programme, one of the largest nuclear clean-up programmes in the world. The conclusions, published in 2002, were surprisingly frank in exposing serious weaknesses in the US decommissioning system. Department of Energy Assistant Secretary for Environmental Management Jessie Roberson commented that the Department of Energy had "focused on managing risk rather than reducing or eliminating it. We have avoided many tough decisions, rather than confronting them. We have not held ourselves accountable to deliver real risk reduction. In short, our indicators measured process not progress, opinions not results.

Obviously, a programme that reports high success in its internal indicators while failing to deliver to the public has a real problem."

Difficulties in the United States have focused on the relatively small proportion of the environmental budget that was actually spent on cleaning up sites. Since the programme began in 1989, only one third of the programme's $60 billion expenditure has been spent on real clean-up. Not surprisingly, President Bush's review team concluded that without a fundamental change in the government's contracting strategy, nuclear clean-up timescales and costs would inevitably increase to more than $300 billion and lead to unnecessarily prolonged and potentially severe financial and environmental risks. At the heart of President Bush's strategy is a shift away from simple management and operation contracts, where fees are paid largely on the contractor's level of effort, towards performance based contracting using fixed outcomes and clear end-points that need to be achieved. In Britain the Nuclear Decommissioning Authority has taken a hybrid approach, where the contracting scheme pays for basic cost recovery with a small percentage profit on top, although the profit element depends upon contractor performance.

Overall, President Bush's policy review concluded that clean-up work should be prioritised to achieve the greatest risk reduction at an accelerated rate, and that performance-based contracting is the single best opportunity for enhancing delivery. But interestingly the Department of Energy also recognised that fee payments may not have been adequate to attract best-in-class contractors. The Department's share of the environmental management market in the United States had dropped from 12% in 1997 to around 8% by 2002. This loss of market share signalled a preference by American contractors to work in other more profitable sectors of the environmental management market. Regardless of whether the US case is typical, its shortcomings indicate that even with well-funded programmes, excellent scientific expertise, and a long history of dealing with nuclear waste, both technological and managerial problems are likely to remain for some time.

Privatisation paradox

In principle the government's new vision for a competitive decommissioning marketplace sounds great for both the nuclear industry and the taxpaying general public. The public gets hazardous nuclear plants dismantled for a bargain price and hopefully lower tax bills, while business gets fair and predictable profits from a long-term work programme. But how well do these business arguments stand up in the real world? Nuclear decommissioning is, by definition, a declining market. In the countries that have developed nuclear technology there are, after all, only a certain number of nuclear sites that will need to be cleaned up. When this work is complete the commercial decommissioning opportunities will be over, unless more nuclear power stations are built that will themselves eventually need decommissioning at the end of their working lifetimes some 60 years ahead. Forecasts of the Nuclear Decommissioning Authority's annual spending show spending levels reaching a peak within the next five years, then falling rather dramatically at a rate of between 5.7 per cent to 6.5 per cent each year for the next three decades. Compared with today, the Nuclear Decommissioning Authority's annual spending levels will halve within the next 10 years and drop to a quarter of their present level within the next 20 years.

A key question then is why would an investor want to buy in to an obviously declining marketplace? The main reason is that government contracts offer companies dependable cash flow and moderate profit at relatively low risk when compared with other more speculative commercial investments. Furthermore, despite the inevitable spending fall as progress with decommissioning gains momentum, the British decommissioning market is actually growing in the short term as nuclear clean-up costs have escalated on average by around nine per cent each year over the past five years. While this escalation is bad news for taxpayers, it is good news for decommissioning companies and their investors. The key attraction for investors is that nuclear decommissioning contracts provide a relatively stable baseload of government-funded work in which contractors are guaranteed to recover their costs plus an agreed level of profit subject to achieving certain performance targets.

At present the Nuclear Decommissioning Authority has pegged the maximum level of profit that can be earned at 4.4 per cent of the annual turnover of each nuclear site. But this margin is likely to rise to between 10 and 15 per cent when commercial competitions for site management contracts have been competed in the private sector. Based on the Nuclear Decommissioning Authority's current £2.5 billion annual spending level, total profits for site management contracts might range from a low of £110 million at 4.4 per cent margin, £250 million at 10 per cent margin or as high as £375 million at 15 per cent margin. These figures are important because the value of a company is largely based on its future potential to earn profits for shareholders. As an approximate rule of thumb the value of a company for sale in the marketplace is normally worth about ten times its net operating profit after tax (NOPAT), which would value the companies running the Nuclear Decommissioning Authority's 17-year site management contracts as worth around £1.1 billion at 4.4 per cent margin. In June 2007 the US firm EnergySolutions bought BNFL's three-year transitional site management contracts for running all of the UK's Magnox sites for £72 million – about 29 per cent less than the expected £102 million contract value generated from annual management profits of £34 million.

Despite these projections it is worth remembering that companies are only really worth what investors are actually prepared to pay for them. According to the *Financial Times*, in September 2006 the American decommissioning firm Fluor offered up to £400 million to buy the decommissioning business of British Nuclear Fuels plc (BNFL), triggering a flurry of similar offers from other investors. The government reacted by doing something very interesting and unexpected: contrary to market expectations of a sell-off, the government announced on 24th October 2006 that it had decided to keep nearly all of the workforce safely inside the public sector, protecting them within the Nuclear Decommissioning Authority's Site Licence Companies. Only nine per cent of the BNFL group's 13,812 employees were transferred to the private sector – 69 staff from the Reactor Sites Management Company, 560 staff from the Project Services decommissioning business and 642 staff from the Nexia Solutions research and development arm – and half of these were earmarked to join another government owned research organisation, the National Nuclear Laboratory. In reality only 4.5 per cent of the civil nuclear workforce had truly been privatised.

Why had the government apparently given up a potential £1 billion sale? The answer is that a sale would have created a paradox at the heart of the government's commercialisation strategy for the nuclear industry. Its largest player, BNFL, would have been worth little to investors if it had no long-term contracts, making the firm difficult to sell. But granting lucrative forward contracts that continued BNFL's existing monopoly position would have destroyed the market diversity that the Nuclear Decommissioning Authority was trying hard to achieve. For the best of reasons, the government had to retreat from privatisation in order to safeguard the future of the decommissioning market.

This dilemma goes to the heart of what the Nuclear Decommissioning Authority is really for. The Energy Act 2004 says that its purpose is to decommission nuclear facilities, promote competition for contracts and secure value for money for the taxpayer. The central plank of its competition strategy is to artificially create a vibrant commercial decommissioning services market over the next decade. But the problems encountered with the break-up of BNFL suggest that the newly created £101 billion nuclear decommissioning market is rather fragile and there may be some risk of market failure – or more likely a market consolidation in which most nuclear sites are eventually run by just a handful of large and experienced companies capable of managing the financial risks involved.

Investment dilemmas

Potential investors in nuclear decommissioning face a fundamental dilemma. In a business environment where profits are set by government under 'cost-plus' contracts, company growth depends on increasing the government's level of spending on liabilities. But from the government's perspective, successful contract management depends on cutting liability costs for taxpayers. Without a shared financial objective it's very difficult to find 'win-win' solutions that both cut costs for government while at the same time allow nuclear firms to grow.

In business there are really only two main ways to increase profits: firms can either increase sales and win a larger share of the market, or they can cut back on costs and make immediate savings by downsizing. When profits grow faster than sales, as is usually the case in the first few years after nationalised monopoly companies are first privatised, the new firms are really growing by cost cutting and downsizing staff. However, the total size of the decommissioning market will not continue to grow but is expected to peak over the next few years and then steadily decline. Because the size of the market is limited, the only realistic way for firms to increase their profits over the longer term will be to buy up and take over smaller nuclear companies, cutting their staff to reduce wages bills. This cycle of company acquisitions will eventually result in a highly consolidated nuclear services market dominated by perhaps two or three larger players that must fight for profits in a steady or declining market as more and more decommissioning work is completed. Indeed the government's 2002 White Paper *Managing the Nuclear Legacy* envisaged a longer-term clean-up budget of only £1 billion per year, less than half of the Nuclear Decommissioning Authority's spend today. This might begin to happen as early as 2012 to 2016 when the Nuclear Decommissioning Authority's spent fuel reprocessing activities are scheduled to end.

Alarmingly for shareholders, this could make nuclear decommissioning companies a rather bad long-term investment prospect on the stock market, because company share prices tend to reflect next year's expected growth and earnings potential rather than today's short-term profits. Shareholders, especially large institutional investors such as pension funds, need consistent corporate performance and steady growth in earnings and market share. When forecasts of a company's future earnings drop, the share price invariably lowers, often substantially devaluing the company. For example, in October 2006 shares in the nuclear electricity generator British Energy temporarily dipped 24 per cent on news of cracking found in some boiler pipes at two of its nuclear power stations.

Despite the apparently large £101 billion market potential over the next century, it is hard to see the real commercial incentives for most companies to enter the nuclear market on the cheap by undercutting their rivals on price, especially when other business risks are factored in. Nuclear companies can suffer from unpredictable and costly regulatory interventions, claims for compensation or penalties from nuclear mishaps that inevitably occur from time to time. For example, British Nuclear Group, the contractor managing the Sellafield nuclear complex in northwest England, was 'fined' a £2 million profit penalty by the Nuclear Decommissioning Authority in 2006 for an accidental radioactive leak at the THORP reprocessing facility. The company was also formally prosecuted by the nuclear safety regulator, the Health & Safety Executive, and fined £0.5 million by the criminal courts. The THORP incident cost British Nuclear Group £2.5 million in penalties plus significant reputational damage. Meanwhile, the United Kingdom Atomic Energy Authority was 'fined' a £2 million profit penalty the same year by the Nuclear Decommissioning Authority for a spillage at a radioactive waste packaging plant at Dounreay. These sanctions illustrate not just the commercially risky nature of the nuclear business, but also how the Nuclear Decommissioning Authority can sometimes act as a *de facto* regulator by issuing market penalties.

Nuclear safety and environmental regulation is a particularly difficult area. In contrast to the United States, the British nuclear regulatory system is based on setting broad environmental goals rather than fixed standards for clean-up. In practice this means that clean-up decisions are made on a case-by-case basis. It is very difficult to pin down the regulators on precisely what is acceptable and what isn't. In effect, the regulators ask nuclear contractors to explain what they plan to do, and the regulators say whether they think it can be done better. Inconsistencies in decision-making inevitably arise. The lack of prescription has hit some nuclear operators heavily in the past. In 2003 a parliamentary oversight report by the influential Commons Public Accounts Committee highlighted a 62 per cent cost overrun of £357 million in the cost of new nuclear submarine facilities at Devonport and singled out regulatory factors as the main cause.

In the nuclear industry, winning public sector government contracts is often crucial for the viability of firms in the supply chain and as a consequence of this dependency the public sector can and does affect market structure by choosing to award contracts to a larger or smaller number of suppliers. It is important for the Nuclear Decommissioning Authority to get this choice right because long-term changes in market structure caused by short-term restrictions or distortions cannot easily be reversed. A particular problem with government nuclear contracts is that the public sector is often highly risk averse and somewhat reluctant to choose new suppliers. In effect, civil servants are worried about taking a chance on new nuclear contractors because any failure of procurement that jeopardises the ability of the public sector to safely provide nuclear services tends to be highly visible in the news media – sometimes with political consequences.

So government nuclear officials play safe: in the public sector nobody ever gets fired for making a safe choice. This risk aversion leads to an overly strong incentive to limit nuclear contracts to large and reputable firms, or to stick with the existing suppliers. The effect is that new or smaller firms often find it very difficult to enter the nuclear market, a situation which suits the existing nuclear suppliers rather well because it allows them to charge the Nuclear Decommissioning Authority higher prices, paid for by the taxpayer of course.

Surprisingly, this situation is not unique to the nuclear industry and is a more common problem than generally realised. The Office of Fair Trading report *Assessing the impact of public sector procurement on competition*, published in 2004, estimates that more than 10 per cent of the £117 billion spent on government contracts each year shows some indication of competition problems where the concentration of government contracts was limited to just a few competing firms in markets not regarded as very open. More recent studies published jointly by the Office of Government Commerce and the Office of Fair Trading in 2006, that analysed the impact of competition on the £2 billion domestic household waste management market since its commercialisation in 1988, found that privatisation has resulted in industry consolidation that has reduced competition, not improved it. The overall picture for financial investors is that at best nuclear clean-up should probably be viewed as a moderate risk, medium-term business investment, requiring good profit margins to make the difficulty of entry into the nuclear market worthwhile for commercial companies.

The result is that, far from privatisation reducing costs to the taxpayer, the bill for clean-up of Britain's nuclear liabilities will most likely continue to spiral upwards – good news for businesses on 'cost-plus' contracts but bad news for the taxpaying general public.

The labour market time bomb

Nuclear decommissioning is a hands-on, labour-intensive business rather than a capital intensive business, based on the dismantling of old facilities rather than building new ones. According to the Nuclear Decommissioning Authority's 2006/7 Annual Report, around 74 per cent of the Authority's annual expenditure is spent on staff and contractual labour, 17 per cent on capital expenditure, and 9 per cent on raw materials. Although regulatory factors can be difficult to deal with because of uncertainty about their exact requirements, compliance with tough environmental and safety regulations is not really a major cost driver – employing labour is – or, more precisely, paying the wages of highly trained and experienced nuclear workers.

Over the past decade the mantra of successive governments has been that the introduction of competition to public services brings greater efficiency, cheaper costs for taxpayers and lower prices for consumers. But although it may seem counterintuitive, the relatively low salaries paid to supposedly inefficient nuclear workers in the public sector over the past 60 years has probably helped to prevent the costs of nuclear decommissioning from spiralling too far out of control. This is because in the past the government had tremendous bargaining power as the sole monopoly employer which helped to prevent wages from rising too fast. Wages would normally rise when there is competition between employers for skilled workers. But because there was little real competition in the public sector, the wages of nuclear workers across the country remained broadly similar. There was little advantage in moving nomadically from one nuclear site to another in search of better wages because salaries would generally stay the same. The situation is similar to the depression of teachers' salaries in Britain where despite a shortage of qualified teachers, average teaching salaries remain artificially low because the government is a monopoly employer and can set its own national terms and conditions.

Over the next decade four important changes are likely to upset the status quo in the nuclear industry, producing a significant escalation of nuclear salaries and greatly increasing decommissioning costs for taxpayers: a projected 40 per cent loss of trained nuclear workers through retirements; the absence of young people entering the nuclear industry to make up these losses; increasing scarcity value of the shrinking labour pool of trained and experienced nuclear talent; and as a result, more intense wage competition for nuclear workers amongst private sector decommissioning firms bidding for nuclear clean-up contracts.

A fact often conveniently forgotten by governments is that competition can mean high prices as well as low. Competitive markets all work in the same basic way whether the commodities being traded are as different as antiques, energy or labour. For example, many small antiques shops have gone out of business because their regular supply of cheap knick-knacks has gradually dried up as sellers realise they can usually get much better prices on the internet auction website *eBay*. Higher prices for *eBay* sellers have forced the middle men antiques dealers out of business. The same effect was seen on gas prices in Britain during the unexpectedly cold month of November 2005 when UK natural gas became the world's most expensively traded fuel, as gas prices temporarily jumped five times higher than average because of concerns that gas supplies would struggle to meet winter demand. Gas prices dropped back only to spike once again in March 2006 during another cold spell.

In his book *The Undercover Economist*, Tim Harford explains that prices are not just set by supply and demand but more specifically by the scarcity value of a product or service. If there's a profitable deal to be done between somebody who has something unique and someone who has something which can be replaced, then the profits will go to the owner of the unique resource. On the other hand when there are lots of people willing and able to do a job, that job generally doesn't pay very well.

In December 2002 the Department of Trade and Industry published an influential study looking at the uniqueness of nuclear skills in Britain. The *Nuclear and Radiological Skills Study* reported that there were 56,000 technically skilled nuclear workers employed in defence, nuclear power, nuclear fuel and nuclear clean-up of which around 22,600 – over 40 per cent of the UK nuclear workforce – are expected to retire by 2017. Unsurprisingly it transpires that few young people dream of dismantling ageing nuclear reactors or entombing radioactive waste in concrete for a living, especially with the added worry of maybe developing cancer if they are unfortunate enough to have a serious radiological accident at some point in their career. In the decommissioning world, "progress is waste in cans," as one senior nuclear executive aptly puts it.

The science and engineering qualifications necessary to do the job are also regarded by students as particularly difficult and somewhat unglamorous. Between 1994 and 2004 there was a significant decline in the number of students taking high school Advanced Level sciences in Britain. Physics pupil numbers dropped by 23 per cent and chemistry by 14 per cent. The heady days of the 1970s when Britain regularly invested £500 million per year on nuclear energy research are long gone. Much of the nuclear industry's vocational apprenticeships and training schemes for young people were closed in the early 1990s after the United Kingdom Atomic Energy Authority's research programmes ended. The shrinking pool of students with a science background will inevitably have a knock-on effect on the number of trained scientists and engineers in the future. The current unpopularity of sciences in general – and dislike of the nuclear industry in particular – is a major factor in the expected 40 per cent decline in the 56,000 British nuclear workforce over the next 10 years. Retiring workers are simply not being replaced by new recruits. Even the less qualified teams of manual decommissioning workers would probably prefer to work elsewhere because of the hassle factor of nuclear decommissioning: typical clean-up jobs involve working in uncomfortable conditions inside protective containment suits within radioactively contaminated buildings. This manual work may not be so technically specialised as that of professional nuclear scientists and engineers, but nevertheless these staff work in a specialised context that is both hazardous and unpleasant.

Against this background there is very little incentive for young people to join the nuclear industry. Given a completely free choice, most young professionals would much prefer the better opportunities and higher earning potential offered in the knowledge-based economy of business and finance. For example, in September 2006 the *Financial Times* reported that starting salaries for some newly qualified accountants in London had reached as high as £65,000 per year. Salaries are generally much lower in the nuclear industry where in 2007 the average salary of people employed at Britain's largest nuclear firm British Nuclear Fuels plc (BNFL) was £42,000 per year. The incentives for young people are clear: they can expect better earning potential working in business than in the nuclear industry, and some graduates can earn over 50 per cent more than the typical nuclear industry salary. Even in other high-tech industries requiring advanced levels of technical training, salaries are often higher – for example in the oil, pharmaceutical and life science industries. The depression of public sector nuclear salaries seems to be a strangely British phenomenon. As a rule of thumb, the salaries of nuclear workers in the continental European countries of France, Germany and Belgium are generally 30 per cent higher than in the UK. They are particularly high in Switzerland where the 2006 Annual Reports of the Leibstadt and Gösgen nuclear power plants suggests average worker salaries equivalent to £63,000 to £76,000 per year.

Given the much lower British salary expectations it is hardly surprising that the nuclear industry is failing to recruit new blood in areas of the country where young people have a genuine choice of different employers. But because many nuclear sites are located in isolated rural and coastal regions rather than near busy economic centres, the practical employment choices available to young people are often limited to careers in either tourism, agriculture or the nuclear industry. As Jean McSorley points out in her book *Living in the Shadow*, the economy in West Cumbria relies heavily on income from employment at the Sellafield nuclear plant and in practice local people have few realistic alternatives available to them other than to work at Sellafield. In early 2006 His Royal Highness the Prince of Wales gave a speech in Cumbria on housing design, commenting: "If anyone needs to know about the need for affordable rural housing you only have to look at house prices and wage levels in the Lake District. I was shocked by what I discovered. The minimum house price is £150,000. The average income is just £12,000 to £15,000." Put simply, despite the nuclear industry being an unpopular career choice for young people and only relatively modestly paid in comparison with other high-tech professions, it is clear that whatever employment alternatives are available to young people in West Cumbria, they are generally much worse than joining the nuclear industry which at least pays over double the average rural salary available locally.

Nevertheless when the looming 40 per cent skills shortage is viewed at a national level across Britain, the future scarcity value of the remaining labour pool of well-trained nuclear employees must inevitably drive salaries upwards to a level at least equivalent to other high-tech industries and probably somewhat higher. This labour shortage may seem like a new situation but we have been here before. Industries worldwide were in a similar position in the late 1990s when COBOL computer programmers temporarily commanded high wages from companies who were faced with the prospect of older computing systems crashing from the so-called Millennium Bug. This led to a strong demand in the late 1990s for experienced COBOL programmers to ensure that government computer systems were 'Y2K compliant'. The cost to British taxpayers was over £3 billion.

The lesson here is that labour markets don't work very well in face of scarcity power, whether that be in computer programming, nuclear decommissioning or any other situation where there is high demand for rare or niche skills that inevitably drives salaries upwards. In the nuclear world, wages will rise, not because companies are generous but because they will have no choice if they want to attract experienced nuclear workers who can be relied on to do the job properly. This will inevitably escalate nuclear liability costs for taxpayers. At first sight this may appear to be good news for businesses on 'cost-plus' contracts, who would make more profit as total government clean-up expenditure rises. However in practice the escalation of wage bills will probably force the Nuclear Decommissioning Authority to re-tender contracts on some form of fixed-price basis that would make nuclear clean-up contracts inherently much more risky. The end result of salary escalation is that nuclear employees might become an increasingly expensive resource, in a high risk business, only marginally profitable for their private sector employers.

Selling nuclear services abroad

Over the past decade the organisational structure of the nuclear industry has become more fragmented, triggered initially by the divestment and privatisations of AEA Technology and British Energy in 1996. The 130 member companies of Britain's nuclear trade body, the Nuclear Industry Association, are testament to the existence of a small but active specialist nuclear supply chain.

Despite the nuclear sell-offs of the 1990s, it is important to remember that the resident workforce at each nuclear site has really changed very little. The corporate logos on pay cheques may be different but the same people are often still doing more or less the same jobs, at the same site locations, the only real change being fragmentation of the original public sector site workforce into a multiplicity of private sector companies instead. In short, the size of the trained nuclear labour pool appears to be relatively fixed at around 56,000 people with few genuinely new entrants into the market. Figures from the Nuclear Decommissioning Authority five-year strategy document, published in March 2006, show that more than half of its expenditure is subcontracted to smaller companies in the supply chain. But it is questionable whether this is realistic because it probably simply reflects the degree of transfer of existing staff from the public sector. Nuclear sites are not yet swarming with fresh faces. Despite the intensive organisational restructuring seen over the past few years, the basic proposition remains that the site workforce does the majority of the decommissioning work and this implies that the labour cost base and maximum profits are largely fixed unless salaries are reduced or some members of the site workforce are made redundant. Redundancies can help firms to deliver short-term profits but the scarcity value of the remaining nuclear workers will eventually push wages up, increasing costs and reducing shareholder profitability over the longer term.

Because stock market investors are only interested in investing their money in profitable companies that are continuing to grow and make even more profits, nuclear firms will need to expand and find new markets for their services. Since the domestic nuclear clean-up market in Britain has a fixed ceiling, the only realistic way for British decommissioning firms to expand is to find new profitable opportunities abroad. It is for precisely this reason that American decommissioning companies are keen to move into the British nuclear clean-up market because their own domestic market in the United States will eventually become saturated with a small number of big players.

According to the Department of Trade and Industry's *Global Decommissioning Opportunities* report published in 2005, some 50 per cent of the world's civil nuclear power stations will close by 2016 and the worldwide market for nuclear decommissioning services is expected to be around £300 billion over the next 30 years. In the countries that have developed nuclear technology, there are only a certain number of nuclear sites that will need to be cleaned up and when this work is completed the commercial decommissioning opportunities will naturally come to an end. Well aware of the declining domestic market, the Chief Executive of the United Kingdom Atomic Energy Authority (UKAEA) told the House of Commons Trade and Industry Committee in March 2006: "Our ambition in a nutshell is that over a period of five years and in terms of profitability we would be doing as much outside the UK as we would within the UK."

But it must be doubtful whether a major nuclear organisation such as the UKAEA can win enough foreign business to support 50 per cent of its 1,600 workforce on overseas projects. Countries that are sufficiently advanced to have developed their own nuclear technology or sufficiently rich to have bought the nuclear technology from abroad, usually have their own trained and relatively cheap nuclear workforce. These countries don't need foreigners to supply decommissioning labour; what they need is decommissioning expertise to train their own people instead. Decommissioning 'know-how' is exportable; decommissioning 'labour' is not. The expansion of British nuclear decommissioning companies into new markets abroad – if it ever happens at all – probably won't involve small armies of Sellafield workers jumping on aeroplanes to carry out decommissioning work in exotic foreign locations. And by the same token, Britons are unlikely to see teams of highly paid European nuclear reactor technicians descending on the Sizewell B nuclear power station to carry out repair work during its periodic maintenance shutdowns. As anybody who has ever signed a company hotel expenses bill will appreciate, it is not economically feasible for companies to deploy large numbers of workers abroad for any significant period of time. The costs become too prohibitive, even for British workers who appear to be 30 per cent cheaper than their Western European counterparts.

The only exception is where foreign markets have become artificially distorted for some reason. For example, in some European Commission funded TACIS (Technical Aid to the Commonwealth of Independent States) nuclear clean-up projects that took place in the Former Soviet Union, Ukrainian nuclear scientists complained to auditors that "we did more than 90 per cent of the work, for which we received less than 10 per cent of the money." Western consulting firms were paid up to ten times as much as the local firms carrying out the decommissioning tasks, a situation that was fundamentally unfair towards the Ukrainians. The only reason the situation had managed to persist was because the paymasters were really European governments who were paying European nuclear companies with European money. Ukrainian market forces had very little say in the matter.

If globalisation means 'the same everywhere' then nuclear markets are not truly global. As the Sustainable Development Commission has pointed out, it is better to think of them as a series of local nuclear markets operating within their own individual cost structures, labour conditions and regulatory regimes that apply in the particular host country. They quite literally speak a different business language. For example BNFL's Project Services subsidiary, recently sold to VT Nuclear Services, partnered with Atomstroyexport and Rosatomstroy for decommissioning work on former Soviet-built reactors in Lithuania, where 80 per cent of the resident nuclear workforce speaks Russian. In this advisory role, Project Services is basically providing management expertise to foreign markets. This overseas business model has more in common with a modern management consultancy firm than a hands-on decommissioning contractor.

Even within the 27 member countries of the European Union (EU), nuclear trade is very limited. It is notoriously difficult to sell foreign nuclear services into France for example, the second largest economy in the EU, despite the very large French nuclear power programme that supplies over 75 per cent of the nation's electricity. The language barrier matters; Britain may be part of Europe politically, but culturally and economically it is much closer to America.

Probably the most sensible strategy for a British firm wanting to expand its nuclear decommissioning operations abroad is to either buy or team-up with local companies employing their indigenous nuclear labour force, and then parachute-in a few foreign managers to teach them how to decommission effectively. This is the basic commercial formula that American firms are using to become involved in nuclear clean-up in Britain today. But even if companies are able to raise the funds needed to acquire overseas nuclear firms, they are not always for sale. Nuclear energy technology is invariably sensitive and foreign ownership usually raises issues of political concern to national governments. Saudi Arabia, for example, prohibits the ownership of its nationalised oil industry by foreign firms despite strong political pressure from American interests to buy Saudi oil companies. Despite the apparent £300 billion global market for nuclear decommissioning services, for many companies the most likely outcome is that expansion of their nuclear clean-up services abroad will be mostly unsuccessful. Only a small percentage of the British nuclear workforce can ever hope to sell their services into foreign nuclear markets. This small elite, the very best of the best managers, will be highly profitable for decommissioning firms. But much of the remaining workforce left behind in Britain will become an increasingly expensive resource paid for by the Nuclear Decommissioning Authority and by the same token only marginally profitable for the private sector companies employing them.

This has some important implications for potential investors in nuclear decommissioning companies. At present there is a great deal of market interest in the nuclear energy sector driven by improved prospects for new nuclear reactor build worldwide. This is why the British government's $5.4 billion sale of the US-based reactor vendor Westinghouse in 2006 was so successful, despite its apparently very high price/earning ratio of 33 that would normally make a company too expensive for a buyer to acquire. The value of a company is largely based on its future potential to earn profits for shareholders. As a rule of thumb, the approximate market value is about ten times its annual operating profit. A price/earning ratio of 10 is usually a good signal that a company is worth buying whereas a ratio of 20 means the company is probably overvalued. By buying at a high price, Toshiba signalled that it expects Westinghouse's profitability to increase in the future. This seems like a good bet because Westinghouse made only eight per cent profit of $164 million on sales of $1,962 million in 2005/6.

While things may be looking up for reactor vendors, the problem for decommissioning investors is that the nuclear clean-up market is not really the same as the nuclear electricity market. It is questionable whether nuclear decommissioning business expertise could be readily applied to building a new generation of nuclear reactors for instance. This does tend to undermine the economic rationale for buying nuclear decommissioning companies unless bidders are confident of winning clean-up contracts from the Nuclear Decommissioning Authority or from winning similar clean-up project work overseas.

The lower market expectations for decommissioning firms is illustrated by the sale in January 2008 of BNFL's Project Services business to engineering group VT. In March 2007 BNFL Project Services reported a net operating profit of £10 million on a turnover of £87 million, valuing the company at around £100 million. Yet VT purchased Project Services for only £45 million, with a further £30 million contingent on the firm hitting certain profitability targets. The maximum £75 million price tag reflects a much lower price/earning ratio of 7.5 for the decommissioning firm compared with 33 for the sale of reactor vendor Westinghouse. Although there was strong interest by four bidders, two factors may have depressed the final sale price for Project Services during 2007: the unexpected withdrawal of two private equity bidders as a result of a wider credit-crunch affecting investors following losses in the American sub-prime mortgage market; and market uncertainty resulting from an apparent 20 per cent reduction in nuclear clean-up work placed with some decommissioning contractors in the supply chain.

Dampening cost escalation

So far we have looked at some of the reasons why nuclear decommissioning costs are rising very rapidly in Britain. The problem of escalating clean-up costs for taxpayers has a common underlying cause – different market incentives. The public sector incentive of the Nuclear Decommissioning Authority to cut liability costs is not the same as the private sector necessity for corporate decommissioning firms to recover their investment by making as much money as quickly as possible in a new and therefore commercially risky business market. Nuclear companies need good profit margins simply to make the risks of doing business worthwhile to company boards and their nervous shareholders. Young people need a realistic prospect of earning high salaries to make the hassle of gaining difficult nuclear qualifications and working in what is perceived to be an unpopular and hazardous industry worth the effort. And in future the declining talent pool of privatised nuclear workers will be able to pick and choose employers depending on who is willing to pay the most for their valuable skills.

The immediate financial dilemma facing the Nuclear Decommissioning Authority is how to reduce the country's nuclear clean-up bill while still paying nuclear firms good enough returns. In 2004 the Treasury set the Nuclear Decommissioning Authority a difficult target of reducing the taxpayer's £73 billion civil nuclear clean-up liability by 10 per cent. The logic for creating the Nuclear Decommissioning Authority, envisioned in the Department of Trade and Industry's 2001 Quinquennial Review, had anticipated even tougher cost savings of up to 30 per cent through contractorisation. But meeting even the 10 per cent target may prove to be very difficult, not least because nuclear liabilities have been growing recently by around nine per cent every year.

Although the scarcity of skilled labour is likely to be a significant driving force behind esca-lating costs for nuclear decommissioning over the longer term, wages are not the whole story. Nuclear liabilities have grown four times faster than Britain's average two per cent annual inflation level over the past five years, meaning that some other factors must be responsible for accelerating decommissioning costs. Precisely what these factors are is not completely clear but they probably reflect some continuing technical uncertainty over the scale of what liabilities really exist and what decommissioning work really needs to be done to remedy the situation and restore the environment, coupled with escalation in back end waste management and repository disposal cost estimates.

Decommissioning has been described as rather like a Chinese puzzle box in which new problems are revealed the deeper one looks, as successive layers of complexity are revealed. Each year the decommissioning management contractors tend to look a little deeper at what needs to be done and then cost the clean-up tasks accordingly from the bottom up. As a result, the Nuclear Decommissioning Authority's three-year near-term cost projections are reasonably accurate but forecasts of the total lifecycle cost for taxpayers remain highly spec-ulative. It is these difficult long-term cost projections that are rising by 9 per cent annually. In September 2007 the National Audit Office, which formally audits the Nuclear Decommissioning Authority's annual accounts, commented: "It is not possible to quantify reliably the impact on the Nuclear Decommissioning Authority's future financial results of the settlement of these liabilities."

In the early years following the birth of the nuclear industry the costs of disposal of radioac-tive waste were not really a major consideration as disposal routes were available for low-level wastes in burial sites and intermediate-level wastes by sea dumping, leaving only high-level wastes from spent fuel needing long-term management. However an international ban on sea dumping in 1982 coupled with greater attention to nuclear decommissioning and disposal capacity planning in the 1990s triggered a gradual escalation in disposal cost forecasts under the 'polluter pays' principle.

The Nuclear Decommissioning Authority appears to be applying a four-pronged strategy to help slow down rising costs: (1) set challenging financial targets for contractors; (2) dampen the escalation of wage bills by increasing the available labour pool, making use of skilled work-ers from other industries and encouraging young people to enter the nuclear sector through sponsored education and training initiatives; (3) de-skill decommissioning requirements by performing the most hazardous decommissioning tasks during the first 10 to 20 years, leaving relatively industry-standard demolition and clean-up jobs to be carried out by cheaper lower skilled workers in later decades; and (4), look for innovative opportunities to apply existing commercially available technology from other industries and countries to solve nuclear decommissioning problems in a cheaper, faster and safer way.

To help apply an immediate brake on costs, in its first five-year Strategy Report, the Nuclear Decommissioning Authority asked its nuclear site management contractors to make cost savings of seven per cent each year from 2006, implying total savings of 35 per cent by 2012. The site management contractors, BNFL and the UKAEA, responded by asking their own sup-pliers to make savings of 15 per cent in 2006. To help achieve this, BNFL had progressively slimmed down the number of suppliers to Sellafield from a peak of around 15,000 in 2000 down to 4,000 by 2006, so that the company can more easily set common terms and conditions and drive down prices.

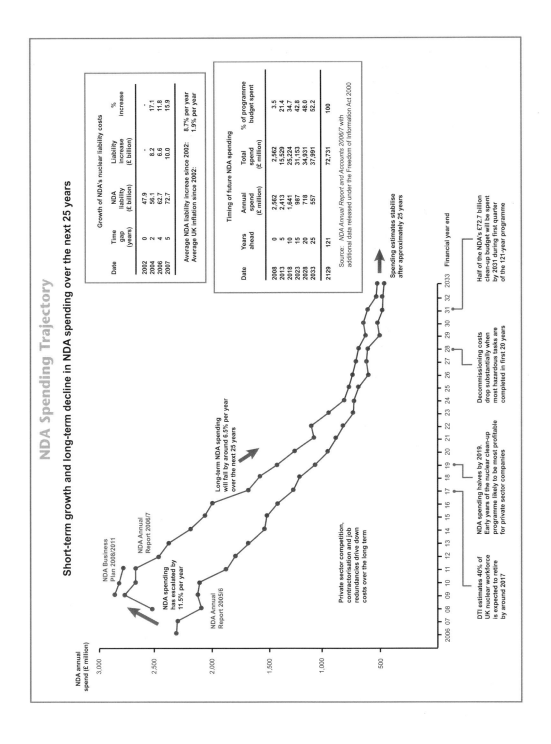

NDA Spending Trajectory

Short-term growth and long-term decline in NDA spending over the next 25 years

Growth of NDA's nuclear liability costs

Date	Time gap (years)	NDA liability (£ billion)	Liability increase (£ billion)	% increase
2002	0	47.9	-	-
2004	2	56.1	8.2	17.1
2006	4	62.7	6.6	11.8
2007	5	72.7	10.0	15.9

Average NDA liability increae since 2002: 8.7% per year
Average UK inflation since 2002: 1.9% per year

Timing of future NDA spending

Date	Years ahead	Annual spend (£ million)	Total spend (£ million)	% of programme budget spent
2008	0	2,562	2,562	3.5
2013	5	2,413	15,529	21.4
2018	10	1,641	25,224	34.7
2023	15	987	31,153	42.8
2028	20	718	34,931	48.0
2033	25	557	37,991	52.2
2129	121		72,731	100

Source: *NDA Annual Report and Accounts 2006/7* with additional data released under the Freedom of Information Act 2000

Spending estimates stabilise after approximately 25 years

NDA annual spend (£ million)

3,000
2,500
2,000
1,500
1,000
500

2006 07 08 09 10 11 12 13 14 15 16 17 18 19 20 21 22 23 24 25 26 27 28 29 30 31 32 2033   Financial year end

NDA Business Plan 2008/2011

NDA Annual Report 2006/7

NDA spending has escalated by 11.5% per year

NDA Annual Report 2005/6

Long-term NDA spending will fall by around 6.5% per year over the next 25 years

DTI estimates 40% of UK nuclear workforce is expected to retire by around 2017

NDA spending halves by 2019. Early years of the nuclear clean-up programme likely to be most profitable for private sector companies

Private sector competition, contractorisation and job redundancies drive down costs over the long term

Decommissioning costs drop substantially when most hazardous tasks are completed in first 20 years

Half of the NDA's £72.7 billion clean-up budget will be spent by 2031 during first quarter of the 121-year programme

The problem with this market picture is that it implies that the current nuclear workforce is staggeringly inefficient and that suppliers are substantially overcharging for their services. Contrary to their popular media image, nuclear workers are not lazy Homer Simpsons. There must be some doubt about whether cost reductions of 35 per cent are realistically feasible over a relatively short six-year period and what impact that might have on the safe operation of Britain's nuclear facilities. Remember that nuclear decommissioning is a man-power-intensive activity where costs are largely driven by the wages of workers. A 35 per cent cost reduction implies a cut of at least one third of the workforce, losing one in every three people currently working at Sellafield and all of the other nuclear sites in Britain. In 2005 the recently retired Director of the Sellafield site wrote to the Nuclear Decommissioning Authority warning that competition and cost reductions might lead to serious nuclear safety incidents, a concern that apparently was privately shared by the government's independent nuclear safety watchdog the Nuclear Safety Advisory Committee, as reported in *New Scientist* magazine.

But to balance these worries it is also worth remembering that some downsizing of the national workforce is inevitable as nuclear sites shift from commercial production to decommissioning mode. According to a 2003 study commissioned by BNFL, following the planned closure of THORP reprocessing operations, the Sellafield nuclear workforce is expected to shrink dramatically from around 12,000 employees to about 4,000 employees, a 67 per cent reduction in the workforce by 2018. On the other hand, the construction of a new generation of nuclear power stations in Britain would further increase demand for skilled labour from the shrinking pool of nuclear workers, pushing up salaries for both nuclear decommissioning and reactor construction projects.

The government's *White Paper on Nuclear Power* published in January 2008 supported the development of a new generation of nuclear power stations, provided that these could be financed by the private sector. The Nuclear Industry Association has forecast that new nuclear build would need an average of 1,400 construction jobs at each new nuclear power station, creating a demand for perhaps 4,200 workers for a likely series of three new PWR stations. This extra labour demand would employ about eight per cent of the current nuclear labour pool in Britain. But with 40 per cent of the nuclear workforce expected to retire by 2017, the proportion of the remaining labour pool needed for new build would rise to 13 per cent if reactor construction is delayed towards the middle of the next decade, as seems likely due to the timescales needed for regulatory and planning clearances.

The demand for nuclear workers might weaken because the construction of new nuclear reactors may turn out to require only a few specialist nuclear engineers and could be mostly undertaken by civil, electrical and mechanical engineers from the British construction industry. The Nuclear Industry Association estimates that a new build programme would probably only require about five per cent of the total engineering resource pool available in the UK. There are a few pinch points where some specialist experience would still be needed, but this mainly lies in preparing complex safety and environmental safety case submissions for compliance with the British regulatory licensing framework. Moreover, if there is a European resurgence in nuclear power then a queueing system will probably develop for orders placed in the early stages of any 'nuclear renaissance', further slowing down market growth. On balance, the overall picture is that a programme of new nuclear power station build would likely increase demand for people with nuclear skills but not dramatically so.

A shortage of supply will tend to push wages upwards in a few key areas such as safety and licensing, but won't necessarily escalate the wages of all nuclear workers across the board.

A more sophisticated way for the Nuclear Decommissioning Authority to cut decommissioning costs is to significantly widen the available labour pool. This will automatically have the effect of dampening down wage-driven cost increases, as nuclear workers will be reluctant to press for wage rises especially if labour is cheaper elsewhere. For example, the Department of Trade and Industry's 2001 Quinquennial Review report on UKAEA suggested that oil industry workers experienced in decommissioning oil and gas platforms in the North Sea could apply their experience to nuclear decommissioning. The logic was that high hazard skills were transferable between different industries. In fact the contractorisation of the North Sea oil industry during the 1990s, which shifted from an industry-ownership business model to a contractor-operated business model, seems to have partly inspired the creation of the Nuclear Decommissioning Authority by the government.

The Department of Trade and Industry's *Global Decommissioning Opportunities* report published in 2005 estimates that the North Sea oil and gas decommissioning market is worth £20 billion over the next 30 years. Developments in oil recovery technology or carbon capture, trapping and storing carbon emissions under the seabed in spent oil and gas fields, could lengthen decommissioning timeframes in the oil and gas sector. The UKAEA has recently had some success applying marine technology to the clean-up of radioactive contamination found on the seabed and beaches near Dounreay in Scotland but currently very few oil contractors have switched sides to the much larger £101 billion nuclear clean-up market. It is doubtful whether these marine technologies could be scaled up and applied to land-based nuclear power station decommissioning for example. Moreover the potential global market opportunities in carbon capture and storage below the seabed, as a workable solution to prevent climate change, are much more appealing to the oil industry and probably a better fit with its core business.

A final challenge facing nuclear contractors is the need to reduce their cost base by applying innovation. As a business discipline, innovation is gaining momentum because it is seen as an enabler. The Nuclear Decommissioning Authority's *Research and Development – Needs, Risks and Opportunities* report published in 2006 sets out the key areas where R&D innovation is needed. Because radioactive waste is extremely expensive to store and dispose of, the overall policy direction is now towards smarter treatment rather than bulk disposal, and this becomes more capital-intensive due to the processing facilities required. But because decommissioning is still basically a hands-on business whose bills are largely driven by labour costs, the innovations will need to be rather spectacular in order to make any appreciable impact on reducing total nuclear liability costs for taxpayers. Decommissioning tasks do not lend themselves very well to automation, and it would not be easy to simply replace workers with robots as has happened in vehicle manufacturing for example.

On the other hand the Nuclear Decommissioning Authority sees more promise in technology transfer by finding existing off-the-shelf solutions that have worked in other industries that can quickly be adapted to nuclear decommissioning. This more commercial market-driven approach seems to be the main area of interest at present. The challenge for site management companies is to turn innovative performance into a differentiating source of competitive advantage.

But what sorts of innovation are really needed? In 2003 the Department of Trade and Industry gave evidence to the Parliamentary Trade and Industry Committee, hinting that it did not necessarily accept the need for greater investment in nuclear research. The Nuclear Decommissioning Authority's innovation strategy should be targeted at practical decommissioning needs instead. The innovations needed are in better management processes rather than high technology solutions – process simplification not complication. Hand in hand with this, business attitudes towards nuclear risk must change too.

In America, risk is not always seen as a bad thing. In fact risk-taking is an essential component of a competitive company in a competitive marketplace. And therein lies the problem: true innovation requires risk-taking but managers in the nuclear industry are traditionally implementers of government policy rather than innovators where often only the safest, and by the same token least innovative, ideas are taken forward. This is not surprising since scientists traditionally favour analytical thinking over the capacity to innovate. Breakthrough answers needed to solve decommissioning problems are unlikely to be found within the continuous improvement culture of the old style British nuclear industry. Better mousetraps won't necessarily make a big difference to the cost of decommissioning Britain's civil nuclear infrastructure over the next 120 years.

The UK regulatory system itself is highly conservative, inevitably favouring least-risk solutions. British regulators are often subliminally inclined towards accepting only the safest option. However, flexibility is the key. The Department of Trade and Industry's 2003 report on innovation, *Competing in the Global Economy: The Innovation Challenge*, identified flexibility of the regulatory environment as one of seven critical factors necessary for successful innovation.

How then, can the nuclear sector innovate effectively? The answer seems to lie in recognising that delivering real reductions in nuclear clean-up costs will require making a break from the past and doing things genuinely differently, in a cheaper and probably unconventional way that may be uncomfortable for regulators and politicians. But not for taxpayers.

Further Reading

The Nuclear Decommissioning Authority: Taking forward decommissioning, National Audit Office, 2008.

S Taylor, *Privatisation and Financial Collapse in the Nuclear Industry: The Origins and Causes of the British Energy Crisis of 2002*, Routledge, 2007.

The Role of Nuclear Power in a Low Carbon Economy. Paper 4: The Economics of Nuclear Power, Sustainable Development Commission, 2006.

D Helm, *Energy, the State and the Market – British Energy Policy Since 1979*, Oxford University Press, 2003.

A Review of the Environmental Management Programme, Top-to-Bottom Review Team, United States Department of Energy, 2002.

Nuclear and Radiological Skills Study. Report of the Nuclear Skills Group, Department of Trade and Industry, 2002.

Quinquennial Review of the United Kingdom Atomic Energy Authority – Final Report, 2001/1650, Department of Trade and Industry, 2001.

Chapter 2

Sites for Sale: Selling Nuclear Real Estate

Decommission improbable

In September 2004 the government's Department of Trade and Industry (DTI) published a six-page policy statement, *The Decommissioning of the UK Nuclear Industry's Facilities*, which followed an earlier public consultation on *Modernising the Policy for Decommissioning the UK's Nuclear Facilities* published in November 2003. The policy statement from Prime Minister Tony Blair's New Labour government was remarkable because it signalled a major change in the presumed fate of retiring nuclear sites – they would no longer be fully cleaned up. The new decommissioning policy statement, last revised a decade earlier in 1995 under Prime Minister John Major's Conservative government, indicated that Britain had quietly abandoned ever fully cleaning up its nuclear legacy; a view apparently shared by the government's independent Radioactive Waste Management Advisory Committee (RWMAC), which had advised Ministers in March 2003 that: "In the Committee's opinion, any perception that sites can be returned to a totally uncontaminated greenfield status, such as existed before the nuclear facilities were built, is likely to be unrealistic for the vast majority of large installations." Unusually both sides of the nuclear debate – private sector decommissioning businesses and green environmentalists – were privately worried: businesses need a level playing field of agreed remediation standards to drive innovation and generate commercial clean-up revenues, while environmentalists want tight clean-up controls to protect communities from what they regard as a potential nuclear contamination threat.

The government pointed out that the new policy retained many of the key principles of the original 1995 policy statement – decommissioning should be undertaken when it is reasonably practicable to do so, regulatory approvals will still be required and plant operators must not take steps which foreclose decommissioning options. But what had changed was the government's view that there might, in the future, be more potential uses for decommissioned nuclear sites than was previously considered in the 1990s, and that site restoration to a standard allowing unrestricted future use might not always represent the best practicable environmental option (BPEO) – a longstanding British regulatory concept originally developed by the Royal Commission on Environmental Pollution (RCEP) over three decades ago in 1976. The government argued that BPEO sometimes had insufficient flexibility, for example in circumstances where it may be more environmentally disruptive to move radioactive contamination from one location to another – in Britain sometimes referred to as the 'Dig and Drigg' approach, named after the national low-level radioactive waste disposal facility at Drigg in northwest England. Instead the government's nuclear decommissioning policy now envisaged a range of different end uses for nuclear sites – ranging from industrial and commercial use to completely unrestricted uses such as for housing, schools and farming – and accordingly that the sites of the decommissioned nuclear facilities may represent a potentially valuable economic resource. The government had in effect put up a 'For Sale' sign and entered the nuclear property market.

The relaxed decommissioning policy has brought about a sea change from a position where good environmental performance that was once seen to add real value to nuclear companies, is now regarded rather less favourably as something of a regulatory straitjacket on nuclear operations – an unnecessary overhead cost to be avoided where possible. Unfortunately there is a common perception in the nuclear industry that safety and environmental legislation is mainly responsible for impeding progress with decommissioning and the high cost of decommissioning programmes. But despite the natural tendency for industry to blame regulators for pushing up decommissioning costs, relaxing clean-up standards may prove to be commercially unwise in the longer term because setting tough but transparent standards for land restoration has two obvious business advantages: it provides a driver for innovation, because without R&D investment, clean technologies don't just develop by themselves; and it reduces total lifecycle decommissioning costs by establishing a clear goal or target for final site clearance.

The effect of the new decommissioning policy has been to create a shift away from a tough but well understood level playing field of fixed radioactive clean-up standards to a much more flexible – but by the same token inherently uncertain – system of negotiated clean-up 'end states' that has now been enshrined in the Energy Act 2004. In theory this flexibility makes good financial sense as it allows the government to avoid expensive decontamination costs by introducing flexible remediation standards that tailor clean-up levels to the specific future use of the nuclear property. Contaminated industrial property can be remediated to industrial standards rather than higher and more costly residential standards.

However where nuclear contamination is concerned, banks and lenders view the situation somewhat differently to government. From a bank's perspective commercial use and unrestricted use are basically the same thing; banks are sensitive to anything less than full clean-up because losses of several million pounds have been incurred by investors associated with only lightly radioactively contaminated properties. The Nuclear Decommissioning Authority's (NDA's) five-year NDA Strategy is required by the Energy Act 2004 to include details of the condition to which each of its nuclear sites is to be restored. The review of nuclear site end states is a key part of the NDA strategy since this will dictate both the likely speed and timescale – and therefore ultimately the total cost to taxpayers – necessary to complete each site's unique nuclear decommissioning programme.

According to a November 2007 survey of preferred site end states involving the Local Government Association's Nuclear Legacy Advisory Forum (NuLeAF), local community representatives of 15 of the NDA's 20 nuclear sites would prefer some form of continued economic development. From a decommissioning standpoint, every site is considered on its own merits, requiring complex regulatory safety cases for the five key decommissioning stages comprising of: plant shutdown; post operational clean out; care and maintenance; plant decommissioning; and finally land restoration. The central question around the negotiated final end state is the extent to which radioactivity will finally be removed from a site and whether any contaminated structures or ground contamination will be left buried behind. This may lead to the development of at least a minimum recognised standard of clean-up for all decommissioned nuclear sites. Case-by-case approaches are inevitably inconsistent and some form of common standard must inevitably emerge if site remediation proposals are to gain wider community support.

In practice land restoration is likely to be a multi-staged process in which the nuclear site boundary gradually shrinks over a number of years, as the lightly contaminated outer zone is cleaned up and sold off, keeping the more difficult inner zone under longer-term governmental control. This is a politically tricky area because regulatory decisions on delicensing and the leasing or sale of formerly contaminated nuclear property often raise difficult questions of public confidence that go beyond purely technical radiological protection reasoning. They enter the real-world realm of buyer perception and market economics, where costs and benefits can't always be reduced to a simple financial equation.

The market for contaminated property

The basic difficulty with the government's commercial strategy for selling off parts of old nuclear sites is that, while the property investment market generally favours flexibility and choice for developers, it is extremely sensitive to uncertainty, especially where potentially hidden financial liabilities from any residual radioactive contamination may be concerned. For example, in his book *Environmental Risk Management and Corporate Lending*, Phil Case, a former Environment Director of the British high street bank Barclays plc, points out that even after a favourable scientific assessment of the environmental status of a commercial property has been completed, lenders funding investment, and crucially their professional advisors, must consider what a buyer would actually be prepared to pay for it, especially if the banks might need to recover their business loan. This is where judgements must be made of market sentiment, where logic and science sometimes have to take second place. Early decommissioning might make sense on financial grounds for a few high land value premises located in southeast England within commuting distance of London, such as Harwell in Oxfordshire or Winfrith in Dorset. But land use arguments stand up less well for the majority of nuclear installations dispersed widely around the British coastline. Even over relatively long commercial timeframes it is hard to see remote sites such as Sellafield or Dounreay becoming diversified economic centres with valuable commercial real estate. Moreover, Britain's next generation of nuclear reactors will probably be built on expanded nuclear power station sites rather than make use of decontaminated land. Construction will take place adjacent to the existing sites, effectively expanding them onto undeveloped greenfield property nearby. Even if proposals for accelerating the decommissioning of retired Magnox nuclear power stations within a relatively short timeframe of 25 years or sooner are successfully achieved, the partially restored land is still not likely to be available in good time for the first tranche of new nuclear stations expected to be built during the 2010s and 2020s.

The NDA *Annual Report & Accounts 2006/7* reveals that in March 2007 the total land assets of the NDA's 20 nuclear sites was estimated to be worth some £3.6 billion, while its decommissioning liabilities were estimated as costing £72.7 billion. The NDA owns 3,800 hectares of land across the UK of which only one third is occupied by nuclear assets and the remaining two thirds lie adjacent but outside the nuclear site boundary. The costs of decommissioning the nuclear assets are a factor of 20 times greater than the value of the land. This simple relationship illustrates a basic problem with the business case for selling decontaminated nuclear property; economically speaking, it is not likely to be worth the effort involved as the government will most probably lose 95 per cent of the money invested in the clean-up operation. Experience in other sectors has shown that the cost of remediating contaminated land is not matched pound for pound by an increase in the residual value of the cleaned up property. An element of stigma usually remains in which formerly contaminated properties almost always sell for less than the cost to clean them up. The financial risks are highest before clean-up, then decline during clean-up, and reduce further still when clean-up is completed, but the cost to cure is rarely balanced by a corresponding increase in the total market value of the site.

This 'diminution value' has triggered a general reluctance by banks to lend money in certain sectors, especially to smaller enterprises where there is greater chance that the business might fail, leaving banks with direct liability for contaminated properties. The lending chill factor experienced in the United States during the 1990s reflected concern by banks that contamination is an unknown, especially before clean-up, and unknowns create uncertainty which is tantamount to greater risks for banks lending money for commercial and industrial real estate.

Unfortunately it is precisely the smaller innovative firms that are most likely to want to locate at diversified nuclear science parks, as the former nuclear sites and their workforce make the difficult transition from 'big science' government-funded nuclear projects to much smaller scale niche commercial science-based businesses. These small high tech businesses face a difficult obstacle: banks prefer to lend money to big organisations who don't really need it. The large, financially robust, well run blue chip companies who are most able to afford unexpected environmental costs are by the same token less likely to default on bank loans, which are backed by various forms of high grade financing collateral such as equity, shares, cash and parent company guarantees. On the other hand, smaller riskier enterprises that might be attracted to nuclear science parks are much more likely to offer only land and property as loan collateral. For these firms it is essential that the true residual value of the land for mortgage lending is accurately known by the bank because these smaller nuclear companies present a much higher credit risk than blue chip firms.

The overall weakness of the government's sale strategy for nuclear property is that the factors which tend to attract smaller businesses to cleaned up sites – low rents, access to a highly skilled resident labour force, collegiate atmosphere, and some measure of local political encouragement usually through lower commercial property taxes – must be offset against the financial risks perceived by investors and lenders of locating new businesses on redeveloped nuclear land. Since lenders provide a large proportion of the capital for commercial and industrial real estate development and acquisitions, the withdrawal of this source of capital could have significant knock-on effects on commercial real estate values and the prices that the government is realistically able to achieve for the sale of cleaned up nuclear sites.

The lesson for government is that it is very difficult to make big money from selling cleaned up land to small businesses. In fact part of the attraction of locating on redeveloped land is the much lower buying or rental cost than prime real estate elsewhere. There are good reasons for decommissioning retired nuclear plants but land and property sales should not drive the UK's clean-up mission. In any case, the economic diversification of cleaned up nuclear sites into science and business parks faces stiff competition from the new generation of smart, ultra-modern trading estates offering ready motorway access and ease of commuting, that are increasingly being developed at the edges of prosperous towns and cities.

Pricing risk

Banks and investors are particularly wary of the possibility of incurring 'direct liability' for cleaning up radioactive pollution on a contaminated business premises. The trigger would normally be a demand for clean-up by a regulatory authority, usually in straightened trading circumstances where a business was perhaps at risk of becoming insolvent or had already failed and gone bankrupt. In this case the regulators will usually want to approach the business's investors, parent companies, lenders and insurance companies to pay for the costs of clean-up. The most likely way for a bank to become directly liable for clean-up costs would be to repossess the land assets of the failed business. But even if the land is not repossessed, simply having an investment relationship may be enough to trigger liability for banks or private equity firms. For banks and investors it is crucial to avoid any implication of direct liability through exercising control or material influence over their borrower's environmental decisions; so much so that environmental lending reports might even be commissioned through the bank's legal advisers to benefit from lawyer-client confidentiality.

The normal separation between the management team running a company and their financial backers is easier for banks who would typically have an arms-length relationship with borrowers anyway. But this separation becomes far more difficult to achieve for private equity firms who would normally be expected to actively help guide the business and its senior management team. It would probably be difficult for private equity firms to simply walk away from any radioactive contamination liabilities of the failed business. Not surprisingly, in a difficult market, contaminated property or even property suspected of being contaminated may be unsaleable or sold at a loss, blighted by its radioactive history. The truth is that in such a scenario losses cannot be predicted. They will bear no relation to the loan amount advanced by the bank or to the original value of the property – they will depend solely on the size of the clean-up cost and the residual resale value.

For example, *The Washington Post* reported in August 2007 that the cost of cleaning up polonium-210 radioactive contamination from the suspected assassination of former Russian KGB agent Alexander Litvinenko in London was $6.5 million – $500,000 for checking and clearing 27 lightly contaminated properties by Westminster City Council, $4 million for follow-up radiation monitoring by the Health Protection Agency and $2 million for the policing operation and investigation by New Scotland Yard. Litvinenko died in November 2006, three weeks after polonium-210 was apparently slipped into his tea in the bar of a London hotel. These costs were realised despite the fact that polonium-210 remains radioactive for only a short period of time. It has a half-life of 138 days, meaning that 50 per cent of the contamination will vanish naturally by radioactive decay within the first five months and more than 99 per cent will have completely disappeared within four years.

But these facts are mostly irrelevant in the marketplace. It does not matter that radiological clean-up costs are usually greatly out of proportion to scientific assessments of the actual public health risk – what matters is the market's perception of the property and the reaction of potential buyers. It is for this reason that a 'dirty bomb' that might be used by terrorists to deliberately spread radioactive contamination in a major city is generally regarded by security analysts as an economic weapon. The blast mainly affects a limited area within 100 feet of the detonation point, but the radioactive contamination plume spreads much more widely, requiring extensive decontamination; the main hazard is to city taxpayers' wallets rather than their health. Al-Qaeda has long made a point of hitting economic targets – the World Trade Center was likely targeted on 11th September 2001 not only because attacking it would kill many people but also because the Twin Towers were symbols of America's corporate economic power. According to a videotape message released by terrorist leader Osama bin Laden in November 2004, each $1 spent by al-Qaeda funding terrorist strikes has cost the United States $1 million in economic fallout and military spending; in a very real sense al-Qaeda is waging an economic war on the United States.

A more practical example of the potential economic effect of radioactive contamination on property value is the Blue Circle High Court Case. In 1998 the British Court of Appeal awarded damages for loss of property value to Blue Circle Industries plc, essentially because of the residual stigma attached to a property from cleaned up plutonium contamination. Following an exceptionally severe storm in July 1989, water bearing low levels of plutonium in sediments from ponds situated at the Ministry of Defence's (MoD's) Atomic Weapons Establishment (AWE) at Aldermaston in southern England overflowed onto adjacent marsh-land belonging to Blue Circle. AWE embarked on a major exercise to remove the sediment and return the site to its original state. All the affected sediment was removed at MOD's expense by 1994. Yet two years later in 1996 the company successfully won damages for economic loss from the collapse of negotiations related to a possible £10 million sale of the Blue Circle estate. The High Court awarded damages in excess of £5 million against the MOD. MOD appealed against this ruling but the appeal was rejected and the Court of Appeal increased the level of damages awarded to some £6 million in 1998. Both sides agreed there was no physical damage to human health, and the area affected was well away from land regularly used by the company or to which the public had access. Nevertheless the property had been significantly devalued apparently by the market's reaction to low levels of plutonium contamination that were in reality only marginally above the regulatory clearance threshold.

Perhaps even more surprisingly, American law courts have actually awarded compensation to landowners even when their land has not been physically contaminated. In 1992 the New Mexico Supreme Court awarded $888,000 to the Komis family in compensation for the loss of 43 acres of their land that had been requisitioned by the City of Santa Fe to build a road bypass. What made the Komis case special was that the road was built to carry plutonium and uranium military waste from the Los Alamos National Laboratory to the US Department of Energy's Waste Isolation Pilot Plant (WIPP) in southern New Mexico. WIPP is a deep geo-logical disposal repository, the first operational repository in the world, licensed to dispose of transuranic (TRU) military wastes. The Supreme Court decided that a loss in value from the public perception of risk to the Komis family's remaining land was compensable and awarded $338,000 damages – 38 per cent of the total compensation package – due to the public perception of risk related to the planned road shipments of radioactive waste near their property.

The overall point is that Litvinenko, Blue Circle and Komis – three widely differing examples of the effect of radioactive contamination on market thinking – illustrate the severe difficulty faced by the government in making a profit from selling or leasing cleaned up nuclear sites to small and medium sized businesses in the private sector. They also serve as warning to banks and investors that it is not just Chernobyl doomsday contamination scenarios that can lead to significant financial losses; even relatively minor radioactive contamination events can wipe out the value of say a million pound loan or investment in a typical small to medium sized business.

It will be interesting to see whether the Litvinenko family home in the fashionable Muswell Hill area of north London – reported by the BBC to be worth £500,000 before it became radioactively contaminated – will still retain this value on the housing market; and whether the banks will offer potential future owners a mortgage on the property. The Merlin family in Cumbria, discussed later in this chapter, lost 42 per cent of the value of their home when it was sold in the 1980s under circumstances involving radioactive contamination from Sellafield.

Delicensing dilemmas

As with many areas of environmental policy, a key question on the decommissioning of nuclear sites is: how clean is clean enough? The UK's Nuclear Installations Act 1965 sets a simple yet elegant criterion – there should be 'no danger' from ionising radiation before a part of the site, or the whole site, can be safely delicensed. The radioactive contamination must be mostly cleaned up and there must have ceased to be any danger from ionising radiations from anything on the site. Delicensing implies the complete removal of the nuclear land from formal regulatory control. But in practice governmental oversight merely shifts after delicensing towards other forms of statutory regulation; the Radioactive Substances Act 1993, the Radioactive Contaminated Land Regulations 2006 and the Ionising Radiations Regulations 1999 all play a part in deciding whether cleaned up land is actually safe to use. Each of the regulations apply their own subtly different legal criteria, meaning that in theory the lowest common denominator becomes the *de facto* clean-up standard.

Nevertheless all of the regulations must be taken extremely seriously because they give safety and environmental inspectors various powers that can ultimately be used to force businesses to decontaminate and remediate radioactive pollution spills if this proves to be necessary – paid for at the company's own expense of course. Although the letter of the law sets the overall framework for controlling radioactivity, experience shows that it is the practical interpretation of legal duties by the regulatory authorities that is of most importance for businesses.

The principal licensing authorities are the Health and Safety Executive (HSE), the Environment Agency (EA) and the Scottish Environment Protection Agency (SEPA) who together regulate the management of radioactivity in England, Wales and Scotland. The Nuclear Installations Act 1965 created a broad system of licensing of operations on civil nuclear sites while the Radioactive Substances Act 1993 established a system of licensing discharges and disposals of radioactive wastes produced by these operations. The Radioactively Contaminated Land Regulations 2006 (through the Environmental Protection Act 1990) introduced a further safety net in which radioactive contamination arising from other non-nuclear industries is regulated by Local Authorities. The Ionising Radiations Regulations 1999 sets radiation dose limits for workers and members of the public who might be exposed to radioactivity from business premises.

Regulatory licensing – in which a business needs a specific safety or environmental licence from a particular regulatory authority before it can trade – is normally reserved for activities which the regulators consider to pose particular safety or environmental risks. The licensing process is the central mechanism for obtaining regulatory permission to operate. At present the system of nuclear safety licensing by HSE and environmental discharge licensing by EA and SEPA both involve a broadly similar technocratic process in which a business makes an application for a regulatory licence, the regulator assesses the application and any supporting technical information, and then makes a decision on whether a licence should be granted or refused. In practice it is unusual for a nuclear regulator to completely refuse authorisation, although the conditions of the licence actually granted might be difficult to comply with or impose tight constraints on the way in which a nuclear installation must be operated – known as the safe operating envelope. Licences contain a number of limitations and conditions on how the nuclear installation must be run. Inspectors from the regulatory body periodically visit nuclear sites and check for compliance with these detailed limits and conditions. Where breaches of licence requirements occur the regulators have a number of statutory powers available to restore compliance with licence conditions and may prosecute for serious licence breaches.

A similar administrative mechanism also applies for the process of delicensing, in which the government or a business would want to voluntarily surrender its nuclear site licence so that in theory it no longer had financial and management responsibility for the site. The main practical application of HSE's 'no danger' criterion will probably not be the complete delicensing of nuclear sites; instead it will mainly be used to help clear or de-restrict certain parts of these sites, so that fewer areas will require permanent ongoing radiological protection, possibly for many decades. The delicensed areas can be made available for new uses or perhaps even leased or sold to new owners.

HSE's policy guidance *HSE Criterion For Delicensing Nuclear Sites*, published in 2005, allows parts of nuclear sites to be delicensed from further regulatory control, provided that the risk of death to an individual member of the public from any residual radioactive contamination present is around one chance in one million per year. HSE's general policy on the management of risk is explained in *Reducing Risks, Protecting People: HSE's Decision-Making Process*, published in 2001, which regards this level of risk as broadly acceptable. It is clear then, that if nuclear sites are to be delicensed, no danger will not necessarily mean no contamination.

The biological relationship between radiation dose and health risk is complex, depending on many factors such as the type of radiation emitted by the radioactive material, its energy and effect on the body, the age of the person exposed – children being more vulnerable to radiation than adults – and whether any radioactive contamination has entered the person's body and spread around internal organs. But as a rule of thumb, HSE's one chance in a million risk criterion is approximately equivalent to a total whole body radiation dose of 20 microsieverts per year. An adult exposed to this level of radiation would have roughly one chance in one million each year of dying from a cancer triggered by the radiation exposure. This dose level has effectively become the clearance criteria for nuclear delicensing in Britain today, although there remains some technical debate about whether it should be slightly lower, of the order of 10 microsieverts per year, in compliance with the 1996 European basic safety standards directive (*Council Directive 96/29/EURATOM*).

For comparison, the legal radiation dose limit for an adult member of the public in Britain is 1,000 microsieverts per year. Depending on a buyer's personal perspective, and especially his or her attitude towards nuclear radiation and cancer, the 20 microsievert clearance criterion is reassuringly some 50 times lower than HSE's public radiation dose limit. It is also 110 times lower than the 2,200 microsieverts of background radiation that British people typically receive each year from mostly natural sources. Viewed from a scientific perspective then, delicensed nuclear land ought to be very safe indeed.

Curiously, the Radioactive Contaminated Land Regulations applying to non-nuclear land allow much higher radiation dose clean-up thresholds. According to the government's Statutory Guidance to regulators, *Defra Circular 01/2006: Contaminated Land* published in September 2006, no remediation options should be considered if the residual contamination were to result in doses to individuals of 300 microsieverts per year arising from the land; and in some cases radiation doses up to 3,000 microsieverts per year might be permissible before there is a significant possibility of harm. The Health Protection Agency's emergency clean-up guidance, *UK Recovery Handbook for Radiation Incidents* published in 2005, goes even further; radiation doses as high as 10,000 microsieverts per year might be acceptable in some recovery circumstances if this would speed up the return to normal living in inhabited areas affected by fallout from a damaged nuclear reactor – or more likely from a terrorist dirty bomb.

But it remains to be seen whether this level of radiation would actually be acceptable to home owners. American environmental lawyer Michael Gerrard points out that public concern over radioactivity stems mainly from worry about its impact on health, particularly children's health, and there is no amount of money that people will accept to endanger their own children. The public response will probably reflect the practical choices available to them; relocation elsewhere if people can afford it, otherwise some form of extended temporary accommodation for families that have few other realistic options. For example, the worst affected victims of the July 2007 floods that hit parts of Britain, moved into caravans during the six-month-long process of drying out their properties.

These alternative clean-up standards have an important implication for investors: as bizarre as it seems, property buyers may need to be extra vigilant towards the possibility of radioactive contamination remaining behind at some former industrial sites and hospitals that used radioactivity since the levels of contamination permitted to remain could be much higher than for a cleaned up nuclear site. There are around 4,000 of these licensed 'small users' of radioactivity in Britain – 100-fold more then the UK's 40 licensed nuclear sites – for example in the fields of medical research, diagnosis and treatment, university research departments, surgical equipment sterilisation, food irradiation, industrial applications such as aircraft radiography, pipeline flow measurement, thickness and density measurement for roads and steel mills, anti-static devices in paper mills and vehicle paint spraying, and in fire prevention applications as part of smoke detection technologies. A surprisingly high proportion of these licensed small users are geographically concentrated in southeast England, where property prices tend to be higher and so investors stand to lose more money if any unexpected contamination problems are discovered. According to the Halifax Bank in 2007, 36 per cent of the UK's £4 trillion housing stock is concentrated in London and southeast England. There are also a small number of former wartime defence-related premises and defence disposal sites contaminated with radium-226 radioactivity associated with the luminising of aircraft instrument dials and clocks. These glow-in-the-dark dials enabled pilots to read their flight instruments during night-time missions, but today they represent a significant contamination hazard.

The recent emergence of national waste strategies for better management of household waste might also in future produce some unintended radioactive side-effects. The modern trend towards waste sorting and recycling at landfill sites could lead to unexpected accumulations of very-low-level radioactive wastes that are co-disposed with ordinary refuse – known as dustbin disposal of radioactive waste – that is legally authorised from some small user sites. The government's recently updated *Policy for the Long Term Management of Solid Low Level Radioactive Waste in the United Kingdom*, published in March 2007, extended the use of 'dustbin loads' and 'bulk disposals' of very-low-level radioactive waste to general landfill sites, rather than require any 'special precautions burial' measures as had previously been the normal regulatory practice for disposing of radioactive waste at specific landfill locations. In Britain a great deal of household and commercial refuse is disposed by landfill, which tends to concentrate some pollutants. Elevated levels of tritium radioactivity have been observed in water leachates from 30 per cent of landfill sites according to an Environment Agency study published in 1998; nine out of 30 landfill sites studied were leaching tritium substantially above background levels, most likely caused by past disposals of tritium-powered *EXIT* signs that were commonly used as emergency lighting in public cinemas. Incineration of landfill waste also concentrates some pollutants in fly ash, which again tends to be disposed of in landfill sites, adding to the overall concentration effect. Metal recycling – which is becoming increasingly popular with politicians and public alike – will in future almost certainly include some lightly radioactively contaminated metals recovered from sites of decommissioned nuclear plants and the clearance of former government and small user research sites.

In 2008 the HSE granted Swedish firm Studsvik a commercial nuclear site licence to recycle contaminated metal at an urban industrial estate near Sellafield. As yet few technical details are publicly available. During research for this book, a Freedom of Information Act request to the nuclear regulator for access to the 1,600 pages of technical submissions, assessments and correspondence apparently held by the HSE was effectively denied unless the author was prepared to pay a fee of £3,175 – more than a month's salary for most people. The HSE's own *Assessment of Application by Studsvik UK Limited for a Nuclear Site Licence* (7th February 2008) was surprisingly slim at just 11 pages, approving the first brand new nuclear site in Britain for over two decades.

In the majority of circumstances the dilution and dispersal of recycled materials or segregated wastes from small users will help to minimise the radiation exposure of the public and so ensure safety. However there are clearly local circumstances where concentration effects might possibly occur as a result of national waste disposal strategies. Property buyers need to be aware of the potential accumulation effects of waste management and any involvement in sorting, recycling or disposal strategies that may have inadvertently concentrated radioactive materials outside normal regulatory control.

In this sense the term small user is misleading because some of the sources used may contain relatively hazardous amounts of radioactivity. One of the unfortunate social consequences of the terrorist threat faced in the UK is that the identity of these radioactive sources and the business premises where they are used – information that was once freely available to a well-informed buying public in the 1990s – has now been removed from public information registers due to national security concerns. The fear is that a domestic terrorist might steal a radioactive source from a small user to fabricate an improvised dirty bomb. The removal of public environmental information is an understandable reaction by government to help reduce the terrorist threat. Nevertheless, buyers of a wide range of commercial properties, and some former government premises now being sold off, will need to take particular care that they do not have any hidden radioactive history. For example in 1990 an Irish steel works was found to be contaminated with radioactivity from a caesium-137 radioactive source lost from a British coal mine conveyor belt. The source had accidentally been sent in a consignment of scrap metal for smelting. The decontamination operation, involving 1,300 tonnes of contaminated metal, took three years and cost in excess of £1 million in 1994 prices.

Sir Winston Churchill's wartime maxim that "scientific experts should be on tap, not on top" applies equally well to today's property market: buyer perception of economic value, rather than scientific assessment of health risk, is ultimately the deciding factor in the marketplace.

Regulatory stalemate

In their 2003 textbook *Nuclear Decommissioning, Waste Management and Environmental Site Remediation*, Colin Bayliss and Kevin Langley – both senior managers at the United Kingdom Atomic Energy Authority (UKAEA) – rightly make the point that risk reduction is not really a driver for decommissioning because nuclear installations are already acceptably safe. For instance it is doubtful that any civil nuclear installations in Britain are in such a poor state that the risks to the general public calculated in their nuclear safety cases would necessitate immediate decommissioning on safety grounds alone. This stalemate is echoed to some extent by the economics of nuclear clean-up: it is generally cheaper to mothball plants than to decommission them, at least in the short term. Delaying clean-up puts off the day when serious money will have to be spent on dismantling the nuclear facilities and disposing of their wastes. The total lifecycle spend will be higher of course, because of the extra maintenance costs needed to keep the plant safe during the lengthy mothballing period; taxpayers will spend less on an annual basis but the total is bigger in the long run. In fact this strategy, known as 'Safestore', has been official government policy for nuclear reactor decommissioning since 1995. Safestore allows decommissioning to be deferred until well after closure of the reactor for at least 85 years until its radioactivity has substantially decreased.

On the other hand, if clean-up is brought forward and completed with 25 years or less – known as accelerated decommissioning – then taxpayers will pay more up front but the total lifecycle cost ought to be much less. This faster and overall cheaper approach has been favoured in America since it was first introduced after a policy review by President George W Bush in 2002. The US Department of Energy programme aims to save $50 billion – around 20 per cent of the total lifecycle clean-up cost – through a combination of accelerated decommissioning and better use of commercial contractors to get the job done speedily. In Britain nuclear contractors making up the government supply chain have begun to realise the commercial benefits of the American model. Delaying decommissioning for 85 years is a sure way of killing clean-up businesses in the supply chain but accelerating decommissioning allows them to grow and prosper within an intensified marketplace.

As a general rule, clean-up standards that might be acceptable for one generation tend not to be good enough for the next. Despite its technical basis, regulation is really the political expression of difficulties with public acceptance. Accordingly there has been a general tightening of environmental regulation over the past two decades, reflecting far greater awareness and concern about environmental issues by the taxpaying general public. Moreover, as nuclear employment inevitably declines during decommissioning, the economy of the local community becomes far less dependent on clean-up income, making them less willing to compromise on environmental issues for the sake of their jobs. The late Rachel Squire MP pointed out that since 1990 around 10,000 nuclear jobs have been lost at the Rosyth nuclear dockyard in Scotland – 70 per cent of the workforce. This has altered the community's acceptance of a trade-off between work and the environment. As the jobs have gone, demand has grown for the removal of decommissioned nuclear submarines and their waste. A similar picture has emerged in Berkshire where the Atomic Weapons Establishment (AWE) no longer dominates local employment. The affluent local community, employed in well paid jobs at Vodafone, Microsoft, Oracle and various other blue chip multinational companies near Reading in southeast England, demand high environmental clean-up standards from AWE. Realistically it is unlikely that a suitable for use approach will be acceptable to other communities in which former nuclear installations are located. Clean-up expectations will probably increase as local nuclear employment declines.

There are environmental drawbacks with delayed clean-up too. Sooner or later radioactively contaminated land and facilities tend to leak into the environment or leach into groundwater at low but detectable levels. The question is not usually if but when. Contamination often spreads, increasing the size of the clean-up problem that must eventually be tackled and paid for by taxpayers. Complete remediation might therefore cut long-term costs. In this sense, risk reduction is not a very helpful concept to use in the context of nuclear environmental restoration because cost-benefit risk calculations invariably point towards leaving some contamination behind on economic grounds.

This approach conflicts somewhat with the market view of environmental restoration which is all about removing the hazard rather than the risk; from a buyer's perspective, environmental protection lies in risk avoidance rather than risk mitigation. For example, during the 1960s the British conducted three separate environmental restoration programmes at the Maralinga nuclear weapons test site in Australia: *Operation Cleanup* (1963), *Operation Hercules* (1964) and *Operation Brumby* (1967). Yet within a timespan of 25 years, levels of residual plutonium contamination that were considered acceptable in the mid 1960s proved unacceptable by the early 1990s. The latest remediation was carried out between 1995 to 2000 at a cost of A$108 million funded by the Australian and British governments. Residual plutonium contamination wasn't good enough for Aboriginal tribesmen inhabiting the former British atom bomb test site in the Australian desert, and it won't be acceptable for banks and property developers spending money on buying cleaned up UK nuclear sites either.

As the financial weaknesses of technical risk assessment are gradually becoming more widely recognised there is nowadays a discernable shift taking place towards hazard assessment instead. Why take a deliberate risk when you can avoid the hazard completely? This is becoming especially true of environmental discharges of radioactivity and chemical pollutants where small health risks are imposed on an unwilling public who cannot opt out of receiving them. It is partly for this reason that some enlightened major companies have been setting zero discharge environmental targets for their commercial operations, a goal originally made famous by the world's second largest chemical firm Dupont. This trend is not just limited to major polluters but is extending across the broader economy. In the service sector for example, which traditionally has a strong relationship with its public customer base, there is particular pressure to green the supply chain.

A visit to any British primary school reveals a surprisingly keen awareness of global environmental issues. These future adults will most likely demand more environmental protection, not less, compared with today's standards.

Nuclear housing

Despite the market's tendency to undervalue property with a radioactive history, contrary to expectations house prices do not necessarily dip near nuclear installations. Nearby housing may even sell at a premium, especially if the nuclear facility is publicly recognised as being well run, has a good safety and environmental track record, no serious incidents, and an excellent relationship with the local community. Transparency and trust are key factors. Nuclear sites perceived as overly secretive or with something to hide are naturally viewed rather cautiously by buyers and lenders. Even if home buyers are comfortable with accepting the perceived health risks of living near a nuclear installation, the lending chill factor may still translate into lower mortgage offers by banks, artificially capping the maximum sale price of such properties in the housing market.

Defence nuclear facilities, experimental research sites and radioactive waste repositories tend to be less trusted by stakeholders than nuclear power stations. But the upside is that it may be possible to snap up a house for a bargain price compared with the cost of similar properties elsewhere. According to one new home buyer living near the Drigg nuclear waste repository on the Cumbrian coast in northwest England: "I don't disagree with nuclear power, I just don't want to live near it. But where else are you going to get a house this size at a good price?" (*The Independent*, 8th January 2008).

The early history of nuclear housing is recalled in former United Kingdom Atomic Energy Authority (UKAEA) public relations chief Nick Hance's 2006 book *Harwell – The Enigma Revealed*. The postwar period saw a rapid expansion of UKAEA, whose nuclear facilities were situated away from population centres in rural or coastal locations for reasons of safety and security. Because housing was in short supply, Harwell embarked on its own housing programme, building over 1,100 homes for its workforce with a further 550 houses built by the local authority and 200 temporary prefabs that were used up until 1991. The early houses were postwar steel prefabs with later homes constructed from modern brick. Similar construction was also undertaken near the Atomic Weapons Research Establishment (AWRE – the predecessor to the Atomic Weapons Establishment) at Aldermaston in Berkshire. Demand for 'Harwell Houses' was high, reflected by an 18-month waiting list for scientists to be accommodated. The properties were rented out by the Harwell Housing Department, which for decades was the landlord for the majority of its own staff. In a far-sighted policy, UKAEA chose not to create an 'atomic city' but spread construction across several housing developments in the nearby towns of Wantage and Abingdon, integrating them within the local community. Some homes were also built immediately adjacent to the Harwell site, for on-call shift supervisors, site engineers, emergency staff and the UKAEA Police Force. UKAEA's housing stock was eventually sold off during the privatisation decade of the 1990s, with tenants enjoying discounts of around one third market value under statutory 'right to buy' schemes.

When they were initially marketed in the 1990s the former Harwell Houses had a certain degree of stigma attached to them. They were generally regarded by locals as being somehow less desirable, cheaper and possibly of lower quality than other newer homes in the Wantage and Abingdon area. But proximity to the UKAEA Harwell nuclear site did not appear to be a negative factor *per se*. Indeed homes in the nearby picturesque 13th Century village of Harwell were much sought after. This remains true today, albeit for different reasons: proximity to Didcot Parkway railway station serving the needs of London commuters and ready access to the A34/M4 and A34/M40 motorway transport corridors through the Thames Valley.

Optimism about the value of property near nuclear sites is not always shared by banks and lenders, the main source of funding for home purchases. In a legal case in northwest England in 1990, the Merlin family sued the operators of the Sellafield nuclear plant, British Nuclear Fuels plc (BNFL) for alleged damage to the value of their property from radioactive contamination. In 1973 the Merlins had purchased their childhood dream home, *Mountain Ash*, a large Victorian house with an adjoining post office overlooking the Ravenglass Estuary. Media publicity about radioactive discharges from the nearby Sellafield reprocessing plant caused the Merlins to test their home for radioactive contamination. Some low but detectable levels of plutonium-239 and americium-241 radioactivity were found in samples of house dust recovered from their vacuum cleaner, which eventually resulted in the Merlins deciding to move home. With the aid of a bridging loan from a bank they acquired another property, *Grass Gars Farm*, but experienced difficulty selling their original property, *Mountain Ash*. Under financial pressure from the bank to repay the bridging loan, the Merlins sold the property at auction at a substantial loss. The Merlins had been told to expect a sale price of £60,000 but in the end the house was sold for just £35,000, slightly over half the market value, to a Sellafield worker. The Merlin family sued BNFL for £150,000 compensation in lost money and aggravated damages but lost the case.

It had probably not helped that the Merlin family home had earlier appeared on an influential 1983 Yorkshire Television documentary *Windscale: The Nuclear Laundry*, that must have contributed toward putting-off some prospective buyers of the property. Advertising property as having a potential radioactive contamination problem is hardly an ideal sales strategy. Yet the Merlins had few choices. Their solicitor advised that they would have to tell any prospective buyers of *Mountain Ash* of the suspected plutonium contamination problem as a latent defect. It is hard not to be sympathetic towards the Merlin family. The original trigger for their concern stemmed from a visit by the National Radiological Protection Board (NRPB) which, with the Merlins' permission, had placed an air contamination monitoring device in their garden. The air monitor was intended as a practical check on how much of the radioactivity discharged from Sellafield into the Irish Sea was returning to the shoreline and becoming airborne. At the time the Merlins had two young sons and the family was worried that they might be exposed to plutonium contamination quite literally on their own doorstep.

Some years earlier in September 1976 the Royal Commission on Environmental Pollution had published the Flowers Report suggesting that plutonium levels in Ravenglass should be further investigated. Today, some 18 years after the Merlin family lost their court case, plutonium and americium radioactivity continues to be found in the mud and sediment of the Ravenglass Estuary. The most recent monitoring results by the regulatory agencies, reported in *Radioactivity in Food and the Environment* (RIFE-12), published in November 2007, report measurement levels ranging from 1,700 to 5,200 becquerels per kilogram of dry sediment at Ravenglass. For comparison the clearance level for radioactive waste given in the 1986 Substances of Low Activity Exemption Order (SoLA) under the Radioactive Substances Act 1993 is only 400 becquerels per kilogram – a level set by the government as giving a radiation dose of the order of 10 microsieverts, which has become HSE's *de facto* nuclear delicensing standard. Even today, some mud and sediment from the Ravenglass Estuary is over 10 times higher than the SoLA regulatory clearance threshold for plutonium in nuclear waste. If the Ravenglass Estuary was situated on a nuclear site, it probably couldn't be delicensed – a fate that may well await the clean-up of Sellafield.

In 2006 Roger Bezdek and Robert Wendling published research on the impacts of nuclear sites on the American property market, debunking several popular myths. According to Bezdek and Wendling, the presence of nuclear facilities has a favourable impact on five major factors that affect the value of American homes: the quality and affordability of the residential property available; well paid jobs and income provided from nuclear employment; access to good schools subsidised by local business taxes paid by the nuclear utility; lower residential and commercial property taxes; and good quality public services and infrastructure, part subsidised from revenues generated by the nuclear facility. For example the wages and salaries at the Department of Energy's Waste Isolation Pilot Plant (WIPP) nuclear waste repository, which opened in Carlsbad, New Mexico in 1999, are more than twice the local average. WIPP directly employs 5 per cent of all local jobs and contributes 12 per cent of total local earnings. The new homes built in Carlsbad are larger and more expensive than the general housing stock, reflecting the desire for quality housing by WIPP employees. Much of the new construction is designed to meet the housing needs of management and professional level staff. WIPP also attracts large numbers of visiting scientists, engineers and government officials, bringing economic multiplier effects from extra business to the local community. At another nuclear facility, a low-level waste repository that opened in 1971 at Barnwell in South Carolina, the average price of homes close to the facility tends to be higher than the average price of homes in Barnwell County.

Part of the reason may be that nuclear facilities tend to be sited in remote, economically less prosperous areas where well paid nuclear jobs can make a big difference to the local economy. However in more populous urban areas in the United States some property values do appear to have been lowered for reasons of public perception, as reflected in the Komis court case discussed earlier. Smaller nuclear sites also have a lesser economic benefit on the local community.

American nuclear power stations tend to employ few local people, instead requiring trained nuclear specialists likely to be selected from national recruitment searches. The direct employment benefits of nuclear power plants are sometimes relatively small and thus do not create large secondary multiplier ripple effects through the local economy in the same way as a major site such as Sellafield or Los Alamos. It must also be borne in mind that the sales dynamics of the property market are different for homes in large towns and cities compared with the countryside. In highly populated areas, people tend to value homes situated in open spaces, whereas in more remote areas people tend to place a higher premium on homes clustered together within communities. Put simply, a brand new nuclear power station built in London would probably lower local property values but a nuclear station built in a remote part of Britain would most likely raise them.

Ask any member of the pubic what worries them most about nuclear plants, and the fear of a nuclear accident is normally high on the list. Against this background, the impact on property prices of America's most famous nuclear accident is rather surprising. America's worst civilian nuclear accident occurred at the Three Mile Island (TMI) nuclear power station in Pennsylvania on 28th March 1979. The second of the station's two reactor units overheated and was destroyed in a loss of cooling water accident that resulted in a partial core meltdown – yet there was no major release of radioactivity into the environment. Around 25,000 people lived within five miles of the plant. Shortly after the accident there was a sharp decline in the volume of residential sales within 10 miles of the power plant, and there was a collapse in the property market immediately surrounding the station. But despite expectations of a major property crash, sales prices returned to normal within two months. The market had bounced back very quickly, possibly helped by a large influx of clean-up workers and nuclear technicians after the accident. The TMI clean-up started in August 1979 and officially ended in December 1993, having cost around $975 million. Undoubtedly the key factor in the property market recovery seems to have been the absence of significant radioactive contamination. This contrasts sharply with the 1986 Chernobyl nuclear disaster, where a 30 kilometre exclusion zone still remains in force around the destroyed plant today. The nearby city of Prypiat, once home to 50,000 people, lies an abandoned ghost town.

Valuing new nuclear sites

The prospect of new nuclear power station build has thrown a much-needed economic lifeline to Britain's soon-to-be decommissioned nuclear sites. Probably the best commercial future for retiring British nuclear facilities lies in attracting major investment from energy firms to build replacement nuclear power stations, making use of the resident nuclear workforce and existing site infrastructure. From an economic standpoint, the government's 'suitable for use' nuclear decommissioning policy makes most sense when sites are reused for continued nuclear activity. The sites can remain nuclear licensed, avoiding the costly clean-up of land contamination to the one chance in a million HSE delicensing standard.

The prospect of major redevelopment for alternative commercial uses, injecting significant new investor cash into the local economy, seems very unlikely indeed. Only the United Kingdom Atomic Energy Authority's (UKAEA's) Dounreay nuclear site in a remote part of northern Scotland had once been mooted as a potential location for a high-tech European Spaceport but Sir Richard Branson's Virgin Galactic company instead selected New Mexico in the United States for its first $225 million headquarters.

The conversion of former nuclear sites to science and business parks is a laudable aim by the government, but this will never deliver commercial success on the same scale as nuclear investment. The capital investment alone in a single modern nuclear power station is worth around £2 billion for a single reactor spread over a five-year construction period. The crucial difference between nuclear power plant siting today, compared with the past is that the private sector, not the government, will be constructing and paying for them. Nuclear siting today is fundamentally an economically-driven competitive process decided by investors, liberalised energy markets and energy distribution networks rather than governments. The siting of nuclear stations is driven by two critical factors: proximity to markets and access to supply networks. Like any market and network situation, it is always better to be nearer the centre of demand than at the far edges. This inevitably favours new nuclear build toward the south of England where energy demand is greatest and sufficient land at existing nuclear stations is available. These factors make new build in southern England the least risk solution for nuclear energy utilities and their shareholders. Access to energy distribution networks is critically important for nuclear generators in the same way that roads are vital for car owners. The key thing is not just the ability to generate nuclear electricity at a particular site location, but also having the means of delivering it efficiently to paying electricity customers.

If decommissioned British nuclear sites are to be reused for new nuclear power station build, the central question is how much would they be worth to private sector investors? This question is important because the value of the land will determine how much money the government can make for taxpayers by selling it, or by renting it out and using the money to pay for the UK's historic nuclear clean-up programme, or for privately held nuclear sites, how much equity the site might be worth as a stake in a joint business venture with a commercial energy utility partner.

An expert group report commissioned by the government, *Siting New Nuclear Power Stations: Availability and Options for Government*, published by the government's Department of Trade and Industry (DTI) in May 2007, recommended new nuclear development at the sites of existing Magnox and AGR nuclear power stations. The Magnox sites are owned in the public sector by the Nuclear Decommissioning Authority (NDA), while the AGR sites are owned by British Energy in the private sector. With their winning combination of available land, grid access and close proximity to markets, the five prime locations are generally regarded as British Energy's Hinkley Point, Sizewell and Dungeness sites and the NDA's Bradwell and Wylfa sites, although both the NDA and British Energy together share some development land at Bradwell. Like any market situation, the key to determining value lies in understanding who is buying and who is selling. Nuclear sites are certainly not commodities that are widely available and essentially interchangeable. They are in short supply as there is only likely to be a small pool of economically viable site locations, probably as few as five for the first tranche of new nuclear construction. This is good news for the site owners because the scarcity of supply will increase valuations of the sites.

On the other hand, there are relatively few potential buyers with the financial muscle to invest the several billion pounds needed to build a modern nuclear power plant. The five leading utility competitors in the soon-to-be expanded UK nuclear energy market are British Energy, the French firm EDF Energy, the German firms RWE and E.ON, and the Spanish firm Iberdrola – all of whom already operate nuclear power stations in Western Europe. Decisions on building a new generation of British reactors will be taken in the corporate boardrooms of these European utility companies, not Whitehall. The total investment cost is a significant barrier to entry because an aspiring nuclear utility company would probably want to build not just one but perhaps a series of three (or more) reactor units to benefit from cheaper economies of scale from placing several orders with a single reactor manufacturer.

From the seller's perspective, the best way for establishing the true value of a rare or unique asset for sale in a specialised marketplace is often through some form of competitive process involving several potential buyers; essentially an auction rather than a negotiated sale. As observers of the auction website *eBay* will testify, competition between buyers drives prices up. The challenge is to determine which utility companies can best use the sites, and how much they are worth to them. This is a difficult balancing act because on the one hand, sellers want to achieve the best price they possibly can, but on the other hand the price tag must not be so high that it restricts the ability of the winning utility company to invest money in actually building the nuclear stations – a situation in auction terminology known as winners curse. The problem had previously occurred with the government's auction of 3G radio spectrum telecoms licences in April 2000. The auction raised £29 billion – enough to halve income tax for a year – but the high level of company debt led to a serious investment crash by telecoms firms.

The number of utilities bidding for nuclear sites is very important as this can drive up the price a great deal. Game theorists Jeremy Bulow and Paul Klemperer have showed the importance of attracting just one extra bidder in a competitive process. If a nuclear site has a true value of 'V' million pounds, a winning bidder would pay only 50 per cent of this value if the utility had one competitor, but 67 per cent if the utility had two competitors, 80 per cent with four competitors, or 90 per cent with nine competitors. (The mathematical relationship is that if there are 'n' bidders in a first price auction for an asset of true value 'V', then the winning equilibrium bid is theoretically $(1 - 1/n) \times V$.) What's more, the linkage principle of game theory tells us that the more the price paid by the winning utility bidder is linked statistically to the valuations of other bidding utilities, then the higher the average price the bidder ends up paying.

In practice, determining the true value of a nuclear site is extremely difficult as this will depend on each utility company's own individual assessment of the future profitability of the nuclear power station over a projected 40- to 60-year plant operating lifetime. The government's *White Paper on Nuclear Power* published in January 2008 forecast that the net present value (NPV) of replacing Britain's 10 GWe of nuclear generating capacity would be of the order of £15 billion assuming a 40-year generating lifetime. This is the government's measure of the expected profitability of the nuclear stations under a central scenario (neither pessimistic nor optimistic) after taking into account the expected electricity generating income offset against lending, construction, operation, decommissioning and waste disposal costs. Under these circumstances a single Westinghouse AP1000 1.1 GWe station would be expected to make a profit of £1.7 billion NPV while an Areva EPR 1.6 GWe station would make a profit of £2.4 billion NPV. But because a single nuclear site might be able to accommodate two or even three new reactor units, the total profitability of each station could be as high as £4.8 billion NPV for a twin-unit EPR or £5 billion NPV for a triple-unit AP1000.

This still does not tell us what a nuclear site is actually worth to a utility but it does allow us to make an informed guess about the likely price range. Because the best sites are in short supply – only five are immediately available – it is essential for a prospective nuclear utility to gain access to at least one of them. This really is a business critical issue for the utility, essential for the viability of any nuclear business plan, because without a site on which to build a reactor there can be no nuclear investment. This places the site owners – the NDA and British Energy – in a very strong bargaining position in which the normal commodity rules of real estate transactions will not apply very well. The price that a utility is willing to pay for access to a suitable nuclear build site is likely to be linked in some way to the profit that the business can reasonably make from operating the nuclear station. This could result in extremely high land valuations. For example, a 5 per cent gain-share of the nuclear utility's generating profit would value a site at £83 million NPV if the land was used for building a single AP1000 station or £240 million NPV if the land was used for building a twin EPR station. In real estate terms, the nuclear development land could be worth between £2 million to £6 million per acre for a typical 40-acre footprint PWR nuclear power station – about the same cost as prime residential development land in London and southeast England according to the government's Valuation Office Agency.

In a competitive process it is possible that a nuclear utility might be willing to pay more than 5 per cent, particularly if the cashflows took the form of a periodic rent based on utility profits, spread over the generating lifetime of the station. Renting a site is a good option for both buyers and sellers because it will generate a steady income for the site owners, while avoiding high up-front capital costs that would otherwise need to be paid by the nuclear utility to buy the land outright. Gearing the rental payments to a fixed percentage of electricity generating profits would also help to reduce the long-term financial risks to the utility arising from market fluctuations in the wholesale price of electricity and any unexpected reactor outages in the future.

As few as three or four nuclear sites might be needed to accommodate twin AP1000 stations or twin EPR stations that could replace all of Britain's 9GWe of nuclear capacity expected to be lost over the next 15 years. But as many as eight sites would be needed if the stations were built in single configuration. Modern reactor designs have much higher capacity ratings, typically in the range from 1.1 GWe to 1.6 GWe, compared with their earlier British predecessors, which have capacities of around 0.4 GWe to 0.6 GWe for each reactor.

Historically, new nuclear generating capacity is often added to the site of existing nuclear power stations rather than developed at completely new locations. For example, Europe's newest nuclear reactor presently under construction at Olkiluoto in Finland is being built on the site of two existing reactor units. Energy utility companies wanting to enter the nuclear market in Britain face a potential problem: probably the best development sites are owned by a major competitor, British Energy – the country's sole commercial nuclear energy supplier. Aware of the market monopoly position, the government's *Energy Review Report* published by the DTI in July 2006 noted that it would be up to potential participants of new nuclear build to discuss with the owners appropriate access to suitable sites and promised that it would monitor whether an appropriate market in suitable sites is developing. The government went on to say that there might be other attractive sites for nuclear power such as sites with retiring fossil fuel generating stations. The government's *Our Energy Challenge* consultation document published earlier in January 2006, had noted that around half of Britain's 14 coal-fired power stations may retire by 2015. Building replacement nuclear plants on the sites of retiring coal-fired power stations might offer similar economic advantages to construction on existing nuclear sites: proximity to markets, excellent electricity distribution infrastructure, good cooling water supplies and a labour force with energy sector experience. Widening the pool of available sites for nuclear build in this way would reduce the scarcity of development sites, lowering the price for utilities to buy them.

If it turns out that nuclear build sites remain scarce and hard to acquire, foreign utility bidders might ask the energy market regulator – the Office of Gas and Electricity Markets (Ofgem) – to intervene, breaking up the siting monopoly position of British Energy and the NDA. Both Ofgem and the Office of Fair Trading (OFT) have statutory powers to carry out market investigations and order breakups if necessary. Ofgem is an especially powerful player because it has legal powers to compulsory purchase land needed for energy development under the Electricity Act 1989. Ofgem has never before carried out such a market investigation on energy plant siting. But there had previously been regulatory concern about the closure of coal-fired stations in the 1990s, when some utility companies had placed restrictive covenants on redevelopment of the land preventing re-use for new generating plant. This partly explains why most gas-fired generation was subsequently built on greenfield sites during the 'dash for gas' of the early 1990s.

The lack of suitable nuclear sites has not really been a competition issue over the past decade because nobody had proposed to build any new nuclear generating plant. However that position has clearly changed with the publication of the government's 2008 *White Paper on Nuclear Power* and it is possible that Ofgem might in the future become involved in an examination of fair competitive access to nuclear sites. The most likely trigger for such a market investigation would be a complaint from a utility company wishing to expand into the UK nuclear energy market. But other companies investing in the energy sector may also have reason to complain. The environmental organisation Greenpeace has pointed out that the grid connections of shutdown coastal nuclear power stations could be re-used for connecting offshore renewable generation instead of nuclear. This is particularly true in Scotland where there is a shortage of grid connection capacity for renewables, coupled with political rejection of new nuclear power station development by the Scottish National Party (SNP) government.

The risk of a market investigation by the competition regulators is lessened by the government's plans expressed in the *White Paper on Nuclear Power* to undertake a high level strategic siting assessment by 2009. This is essentially a screening exercise for candidate sites nominated by site owners and potential utility investors. This is mainly a policy driven assessment designed to rule out environmentally unacceptable or technically infeasible sites, leaving the final choice of investment locations to the market. But ultimately only a few of these will be economically viable for investors. For example, despite its substantial nuclear workforce, the remote Sellafield complex in northwest England is a poor location for a modern nuclear power station because its electricity transmission infrastructure cannot carry the energy output of a large nuclear station. Securing planning permissions from Cumbria County Council and capital investment from National Grid for major transmission upgrade stretching across the Lake District are key logistical and economic barriers at Sellafield.

The NDA's first five-year strategy published in March 2006 was distinctly neutral on any involvement with new nuclear build projects, regarding them as 'an issue clearly outside our remit'. Two years later that position had changed substantially with the publication of the NDA's *Business Plan 2008-2011* in March 2008. In a surprising move for an agency dedicated to nuclear decommissioning, the *Business Plan* set out goals to maximise commercial revenue which included engagement with potential developers and operators of nuclear plants to maximise income from NDA sites that could host new generating facilities. Two factors are driving renewed interest by the NDA in new nuclear build: the need to generate commercial income to help fund the government's UK-wide nuclear clean-up programme; and the socio-economic need to offset expected future job losses at NDA sites transitioning from operations to decommissioning. Indeed there has been strong pressure by some members of the NDA's National Stakeholder Group (NSG) for the NDA to consider just giving the land up for a nominal price to utility businesses if this will help promote socio-economic regeneration. The NDA responded that properties have to go on the open market and that the NDA would like to retain some of the income for site management. Leasing land for new build seems to be the best option because this would generate long-term income for the NDA, whereas the income received from a direct sale of the land would simply divert to the Treasury, which receives the cash from disposal of any surplus NDA assets under the Energy Act 2004. The Treasury would probably want to sell new build sites to release their value for taxpayers, whereas the NDA would want to rent them out keeping the cash to fund decommissioning work.

The NDA's 2005 *Management Statement and Financial Memorandum* – the financial rules set by the government on the operation of the NDA – specifies conditions on the disposal of surplus assets and proceeds from disposal of assets, which essentially require that the NDA's assets will usually be sold by auction or competitive tender and will be sold for the best price, taking into account any costs of sale and high value. The NDA can retain sales receipts only if these do not exceed 3 per cent of the NDA's funding – capping sales at around £74 million per year on annual funding of £2,472 million in 2007/8 – with the caveat that sales proceeds over £1 million must be surrendered to the government who will consider whether to reimburse them to the NDA.

An outright sale of NDA land is also attractive from a state aid perspective because it would avoid the NDA becoming directly involved in new electricity generation activities that may be prohibited under the terms of the European Commission's (EC's) April 2006 state aid decision – *Commission Decision of 4 April 2006 on the State Aid which the United Kingdom is planning to implement for the establishment of the Nuclear Decommissioning Authority*. State aid, where governments subsidise commercial companies using taxpayers' money, is unlawful because it breaches European Union competition law. It would not be fair on other commercial energy utility companies if the government subsidised the costs of running the NDA's Magnox nuclear power stations for example. A state aid investigation was triggered in December 2004 following a complaint from Greenpeace that the government might subsidise the commercial businesses of the NDA, principally the remaining Magnox nuclear power stations, the THORP spent fuel reprocessing plant and the Sellafield MOX Plant (SMP). Because all of the Magnox stations were scheduled to close by 2010 anyway, the UK government gave an undertaking to the EC that the NDA will not start any new electricity generation activities nor build any other new assets. The Commission had considered requiring the NDA to shut down the Magnox stations but decided against this measure partly because of the assurances given by the government on early Magnox closure. While the European Commission's final decision did not expressly prohibit future NDA involvement in new nuclear build, the NDA's planned exit from Magnox electricity generation by 2010 was clearly an important background factor.

With nuclear site valuations potentially in the range from £83 million NPV for a small station to £240 million NPV for a large one, it seems most likely that some form of government sale process may well occur in which access to an NDA site for new nuclear build is granted to the highest bidder – with the lion's share of the cash proceeds probably going to the Treasury to help fend off the threat of national economic recession and to avoid potentially messy state aid complications for the NDA.

For British Energy, the siting game is played differently. The 2002 financial rescue of British Energy has left the company in a weaker position to invest than its bigger European energy utility competitors. Instead, British Energy's sites and staff are its trump card for building the next generation of nuclear power stations; the company has a portfolio of eight nuclear development sites that might be worth around £1.9 billion in total, assuming the land value of each site is worth £240 million for a large twin-unit EPR station or triple-unit AP1000 station. British Energy will want to get the best deal it can negotiate with partners, not necessarily in cash, but probably as a significant equity stake in a nuclear generation partnership with one or more utility companies. But British Energy is vulnerable to takeover. In March 2008 the government announced a possible sale of its remaining 35 per cent shareholding. Under stock exchange takeover rules, any energy firm buying the government's entire stake in British Energy would immediately be required to launch a full offer for the whole company. In April 2008 British Energy's share price jumped to 741p on news that the company was in takeover talks – valuing the market capitalisation of the company at £7.6 billion, (£11.7 billion once the government's 35 per cent equity stake is taken into account), with roughly one quarter of the £7.6 billion being the value of its development land for new nuclear build. Yet a foreign takeover to form a Euro-British super-utility raises significant competition problems, since British Energy's obvious nuclear siting monopoly won't be resolved unless the company's development sites are broken up fairly. Unless energy utility bidders can reach an agreement to share the sites between them, an Ofgem or OFT investigation of the nuclear energy market looks on the cards.

Further Reading

K Steiglitz, *Snipers, Shills and Sharks: eBay and Human Behavior*, Princeton University Press, 2007.

R Bezdek and R Wendling, *The Impacts of Nuclear Facilities on Property Values and Other Factors in the Surrounding Communities*, International Journal of Nuclear Governance, Economy and Ecology, 2006.

T Jackson, *The Effects of Environmental Contamination on Real Estate: A Literature Review*, Journal of Real Estate Literature, 2001.

P Case, *Environmental Risk Management and Corporate Lending: A Global Perspective*, Woodhead Publishing, 1999.

Chapter 3

Pricing Waste: The Economics of Nuclear Repositories

Time machines

Few issues are more politically controversial than the disposal of nuclear waste. To their opponents they are toxic waste dumps, symbolising a deadly radioactive time bomb ready to silently release an invisible killer on future generations of unborn children. To governments they are waste repositories, intended to provide safe effective containment for millennia in sites deep underground that are amongst the most scientifically researched and complex engineered structures in the world. Nuclear waste repositories are not popular with the public. Nor are they obvious vote winners. Politicians who are openly supportive of nuclear energy must tread carefully over the tricky question of where to site a national nuclear waste disposal facility. Some 440 civil nuclear power stations operate globally today. But as yet no commercial facility for disposal of their spent fuel waste has opened anywhere in the world.

The only operational nuclear waste repository worldwide, the $2 billion military Waste Isolation Pilot Plant (WIPP) situated remotely in the American desert near Carlsbad, New Mexico, is 20 miles from the nearest town, buried 2,000 feet deep in an ancient salt formation 250 million years old. The site was originally selected in 1974 and eventually opened 25 years later in 1999 after a complex political and regulatory licensing process. The theory behind WIPP is that after military plutonium and uranium wastes are emplaced in the facility, the rock salt will eventually collapse around them, forming a tight cocoon that seals them off and prevents their escape. It is expected that less than a century after the final waste drum is buried, the plutonium and uranium will be completely encapsulated, hopefully for all time.

But WIPP is the exception rather than the rule. In Britain most higher-level radioactive waste is still held in storage at the nuclear sites where they were produced as a by-product of nuclear operations. The government's repository siting consultation document *Managing Radioactive Waste Safely: a Framework for Implementing Geological Disposal*, published in June 2007, explains that as one of the pioneers of nuclear technology, the UK has accumulated a substantial legacy of radioactive waste from a variety of different nuclear programmes, both civil and defence related. Over 80 per cent of this waste has yet to be generated as it still forms part of existing nuclear facilities and will only become waste over the next century or so as these plants are decommissioned and cleaned up. In July 2006 the government's independent Committee on Radioactive Waste Management (CoRWM) reported that only 80,000 cubic metres of higher-level nuclear waste had been generated so far. The final total after decommissioning was likely to be 478,000 cubic metres – roughly five times the volume of London's Royal Albert Hall – with probably another 1.5 million cubic metres of lightly contaminated low-level waste (LLW) from land restoration that will also need to be managed somehow. Of the 478,000 cubic metres of nuclear waste destined for a deep repository, 74 per cent of the volume is intermediate-level waste (ILW) containing about three per cent of the total radioactivity in the repository, while two per cent of the volume is spent reactor fuel and high-level waste (HLW) from reprocessing containing 92 per cent of the repository's radioactivity. The remaining five per cent of the radioactive inventory comes from plutonium and uranium stockpiles, if these are eventually declared as waste by the government.

Environmental groups tend to worry most about any possible leakage of the highly concentrated spent fuel and reprocessing wastes but the overall scale and cost of a waste repository is mainly determined by the need to house the much larger volume of ILW. In the context of radioactive waste management the term disposal generally means the permanent emplacement of radioactive waste in a specialised facility, deep underground, without the intention of retrieving it later. Disposal is intended to be a final, irrevocable step requiring a high degree of confidence by the government that the disposed waste will not provide any future safety hazard to citizens. The key difficulty is that some nuclear wastes remain radioactive and continue to require effective containment or isolation for many thousands of years. For example the radiological hazard from spent nuclear fuel reduces to background levels similar to the uranium ore from which it was originally mined only after about 100,000 years; a timescale that is 20 times longer than recorded human history. Probably the best known and amongst the most toxic of radioactive substances, plutonium-239 discovered in secret by Glenn Seaborg in 1940 during the development of the first American atomic bomb, has a half life of 24,100 years. Half of any plutonium waste buried today would still exist in 24,000 years time and it would take one quarter of a million years (ten half lives) to completely disappear through natural radioactive decay; a similar timescale to the emergence of the first human beings, *Homo sapiens*, in Africa some 200,000 years ago. To help illustrate the point, the British environmental organisation Friends of the Earth – experts at good sound bites – published a cartoon showing a Roman Centurion protecting a nuclear waste drum with the caption: "If the Romans had nuclear energy, we would still be guarding their waste today" – a public message that is essentially correct. A drum of plutonium waste buried at the time of the birth of Jesus Christ would still contain 94 per cent of its original radioactivity if it were dug up today, assuming of course that there had been no leakage of its contents into the surrounding environment. In its 2003 report, *One Step at a Time: The Staged Development of Geologic Repositories for High-Level Radioactive Waste*, the US National Academies of Science, Engineering and Medicine described the technical challenges of building a nuclear waste repository for America's commercial nuclear wastes as of similar complexity to NASA's International Space Station programme.

Imperfect worlds

The single most difficult question that has blocked repository development worldwide is: how can safety be scientifically proved for a period twice as long as the recorded history of mankind? The problem is one of scientific confidence, not engineering capability. As a construction project, building a repository is relatively straightforward, similar to a deep coal mine with its familiar network of access shafts, tunnels and storage vaults extending outwards into the local geology. The major difficulty is not building a repository but guaranteeing to regulators and politicians that it will remain safe indefinitely. The basic problem is that mines tend to be wet, and water is bad news for radioactivity. A weekend tourist visit to any of the disused copper or slate mines in Wales will very quickly give an appreciation of the kind of long-term water infiltration and flooding problems that bedevil British mine workings. It is no coincidence that the American WIPP repository was constructed deep beneath an arid desert. The dry desert-like regions of southern Spain, the Australian Outback, and the Great Basin and Mojave deserts in North America may ultimately offer the best technical prospect for shared underground disposal facilities, at least amongst friendly Western nuclear states. Much of the British repository research effort today is focused on mathematical modelling of the hydrogeology surrounding possible UK disposal sites, simulating the complex behaviour of radioactive pollutants as water infiltrates the repository site and the waste drums inevitably leak and break down, releasing their radioactive contents. Even for a well-sited and well-designed facility, radioactive releases are inevitable but will occur only in the far future when much of the radioactivity will have decayed.

No fixed cutoff time is set by British environmental regulators for the application of radiation protection standards following the closure of a radioactive waste repository. Instead radiation doses and their associated risks must be assessed at their maximum value – called peak risk – which is likely to occur several hundred thousand years into the future. The radiological risk target used in repository risk assessments is the risk to the general public of developing a fatal cancer from exposure to any radiation that might have leaked from the repository. British repository designs and nuclear waste packing standards are intended to restrict peak radiological risks – the risk of dying from exposure to any leaked radioactive contamination – to below one chance in one million per year. Computer simulations of repository leakage show that an initial peak risk of about one chance in ten million typically occurs around 100,000 years into the future, mainly caused by iodine-129 and chlorine-36 contamination escaping from the repository site. The risk then dips slightly before gradually increasing to a maximum peak of one chance in one million around 800,000 years into the future, mostly caused by uranium and thorium daughters and neptunium-237 contamination escaping from the repository.

Of course what a repository site will actually look like 800,000 years into the future is anybody's guess. The worry is that such computer modelling forecasts of the very long-term future are uncertain. Even with the best available computers it is extremely difficult for mathematical models to reliably predict future changes in such everyday issues as stock market share values, oil and gas prices, commodities prices, inflation levels, interest rates and many other situations where the outcome depends on the interaction of many complex factors. Part of the controversy surrounding the scale of the impact of global climate change on humanity within the next 50 to 100 years arises from uncertainties in climate forecasting models used by high performance computers. If computers can't predict stock market prices or hurricane trajectories as early as next week, how reliable are forecasts of radioactive waste leakage thousands of years into the future?

Politicians sometimes assume that even if computer predictions of repository leakage are a bit fuzzy, the likely outcomes will cluster around the central prediction. But actually there are some alternative, very different scenarios – called dose realisations amongst repository modelling experts – which depending on how the repository leaks, can cause markedly higher radiation doses to people living in the future. These leakage scenarios can cause radiation doses up to ten times higher than today's 1,000 microsievert radiation dose limit for members of the British public, although it will be our future descendants, not us, who might be exposed to them. The problem with traditional forecasting is that it is based on the assumption that the current state of affairs will remain more or less the same as the past – geology, hydrogeology, waste chemistry, bioecology and climate for example – but as soon as the environment loses its stability, forecasts become unreliable. Repository designers have to plan for a future without knowing quite what it might be.

The oil company Shell originally developed scenario planning in the 1970s as an alternative way of preparing for the future. The type of scenario planning developed at Shell was built around the assumption that that the environment will definitely change. Rather than trying to remove uncertainty, the challenge is to accept and try to understand it. The aim is not necessarily to 'get it right', but to illustrate the major forces driving the repository system, their interrelationships and the critical uncertainties. Unfortunately, scenario planning is far from being a modern day crystal ball. But it can warn of what major events might happen in a repository's lifetime, so that the hazards to people can hopefully be designed out.

Politicians, regulators and the public have good reason then to be cautious before building a British nuclear waste repository – something that is likely to remain permanent for the rest of human history – whose safety is mostly predicated on assurances based on expert judgement, imperfect computer simulations and in truth a degree of luck.

Bargaining power

Against this difficult political and scientific background, in 2003 Tony Blair's 'New Labour' government began a £6.5 million 'back to basics' public consultation lasting three years to find a publicly acceptable final solution to radioactive waste disposal. The findings of the government's independent Committee on Radioactive Waste Management (CoRWM), published in a comprehensive 232-page report to Ministers, *Managing Our Radioactive Waste Safely*, in July 2006, recommended geological disposal as the best available approach. The recommendation was swiftly accepted by government in its *Response to the Report and Recommendations from the Committee on Radioactive Waste Management* published in October 2006, giving executive responsibility for actually building a repository to the Nuclear Decommissioning Authority (NDA). CoRWM would keep some independent oversight, reporting to Ministers. The government would retain responsibility for finding a repository site and negotiating with the host community.

CoRWM's recommendation to build a geological repository was in some ways surprising because the previous government, under Conservative Prime Minister John Major, had refused planning permission for a nearly identical deep waste repository to be built at Gosforth near Sellafield in 1997. After a detailed public inquiry the Conservative Secretary of State for the Environment, John Gummer, refused planning permission for the Nuclear Industry Radioactive Waste Executive (NIREX) to build a Rock Characterisation Facility (RCF) – an underground rock laboratory widely regarded as a precursor to the development of a national deep waste repository. Although the outcome of planning inquiries does not set legally binding precedent, for example preventing the development of similar facilities elsewhere, in practice the recommendations and decisions from planning inquiries are highly persuasive. The failure of the NIREX public inquiry probably still represents a significant hurdle for the developers of any new deep geological repository site to overcome in Cumbria.

Nevertheless it is important to remember that the failure of the NIREX public inquiry was mainly caused by technical issues and safety assessment uncertainties related specifically to the local geology of the Sellafield site rather than fundamental problems with the deep disposal concept. Indeed the Local Planning Authority, Cumbria County Council had summarised its case against NIREX at the public inquiry as "a poor site, chosen for the wrong reasons." The principal technical difficulties identified at the NIREX public inquiry were: the reliability of multiple barrier geological containment was difficult to prove, risking early release of radionuclides into the geological environment; it was difficult to be certain that the repository access shafts could be hydraulically sealed, risking rapid return of radionuclides to the surface of the earth through leakage pathways; and that the rock geology and groundwater flow hydrogeology underlying the Sellafield site was complex, resulting in wide uncertainties within safety and environmental risk assessment calculations of projected radiation doses to humans from leakage or early escape of radionuclides in the repository.

Although NIREX failed to secure planning permission, it worked hard over the next decade to work with the public to build a better understanding of the socio-political aspects of radioactive waste management. Following CoRWM's July 2006 recommendation for geological disposal, NIREX's technical expertise was subsequently merged with the NDA in April 2007, becoming its specialist Radioactive Waste Management Directorate (RWMD). The marriage is likely to be temporary because RWMD operates on a semi-autonomous basis, ready for the day when a repository site become available. The NDA will then establish a repository Site Licence Company (SLC) as a business subsidiary to outsource construction contracts with the supply chain. The SLC is expected to compete 90 per cent of the repository development, design and construction activity with suppliers. Future separation of the repository SLC from the NDA looks inevitable, not least because NIREX itself had recommended the idea. An influential legal opinion commissioned by NIREX from the nuclear lawyer Stephen Tromans and Barrister Christopher Katkowski QC in 2006 had recommended that NIREX (now the repository SLC) should be independent of the NDA.

Despite CoRWM's affirmation of geological disposal as the best available solution for nuclear waste management, CoRWM's recommendations included three important caveats: (1) that the government should build interim waste stores with a lifetime of 100 years as a contingency that a suitable repository site might not become available; (2) local communities should be asked to volunteer to host a repository in return for a compensating package of community benefits; and (3) communities should have a right of veto and be able to withdraw from the government's site-selection process if they chose to do so. There was no mention of the likely magnitude of repository costs, the size of the community benefits package on offer or the level of value for money for the taxpayer in the entire report. CoRWM had effectively written a blank cheque, putting communities firmly in the driving seat. Whether by accident or design, CoRWM had introduced a new market framework for waste disposal that placed communities in a very strong bargaining position. The tables had turned. For a government more used to finding itself receiving large cash payments from privatising valuable public goods, this was new territory. The government had itself become a potential buyer of a unique and almost certainly very expensive asset – the rights to site a national nuclear waste repository in Britain.

The internal market for waste

Radioactive waste management has become the single largest segment of the total cost structure of nuclear decommissioning projects. According to the Nuclear Decommissioning Authority's (NDA's) *Annual Report & Accounts 2006/7* published in October 2007, 30 per cent (£22 billion) of the NDA's £73 billion nuclear liability will be spent on waste and nuclear materials management. The cost of hands-on decommissioning comes in a surprising second place at only 21 per cent (£15 billion) of the total clean-up bill. A similar picture is reflected internationally. A 2003 study by the Nuclear Energy Agency (NEA) of the Organisation for Economic Co-operation and Development (OECD), *Decommissioning Nuclear Power Plants – Policies, Strategies and Costs*, found that reactor decommissioning costs were dominated by waste treatment and disposal costs (43 per cent) and labour costs (35 per cent).

Although the British nuclear industry has operated for over 60 years, it was not until 1995 that a market-based system was first introduced for managing nuclear wastes. Conservative Prime Minister John Major's *Review of Radioactive Waste Management Policy: Final Conclusions* White Paper, published in July 1995, directly applied the principles of sustainable development to radioactive waste management policy, including a key requirement that the 'polluter pays' for radioactive waste liabilities. Dictionary definitions vary but sustainability basically means running major activities in a way that in principle could go on forever or at least for the foreseeable future. The polluter pays requirement was largely symbolic because most intermediate- and high-level waste remained stored on nuclear sites anyway rather than be disposed offsite. The only previously available disposal route for intermediate-level waste, sea dumping in marine trenches, had been abandoned by the government in 1984. In any case the government owned most nuclear sites itself and so was financially responsible for their clean-up. The only significant wastes outside public ownership derived from the operation of British Energy's nuclear power stations, although today the government underwrites these costs if British Energy's Nuclear Liabilities Fund (NLF) cannot fully repay them.

The application of the polluter pays principle to nuclear sites brought about a significant change by creating a highly effective internal market for waste. After government funding for the United Kingdom Atomic Energy Authority's (UKAEA's) nuclear energy research functions had ended in 1991, decommissioning projects were placed on a much stronger commercial footing with business overheads and waste costs properly factored in. For example, the Culham Harwell Radwaste Service (CHRS), once a free resource taken for granted by Harwell research scientists, now began recovering its costs by charging internal customers for waste management services according to the number and volume of waste drums they generated. These fees appeared on the internal 'cost centre' balance sheets of decommissioning projects, along with many other overheads such as professional staff costs, administrative support, health physics services, laboratory rental costs, capital equipment purchases and various sundries all necessary to run any large project. The CHRS charging scheme had incentivised scientists to reduce the amount of nuclear waste they produced. Research scientists who previously had a somewhat *laissez-faire* attitude towards radioactive waste management now both had to quality assure their waste and pay for the privilege of disposing of it (although in reality much remained stored on the Harwell site). In the run-up to the part privatisation of UKAEA in 1996, these waste charges helped to drive a far better cost control culture amongst Harwell staff because they directly affected the financial bottom line of nuclear projects: in theory lower waste costs meant more money available for interesting scientific work often in the guise of decommissioning research.

The general trend over the past decade is that better waste management practices coupled with higher disposal prices within the internal market created by the polluter pays system, have reduced the annual rates of disposal of radioactive waste. The volume of radioactive waste that has been consigned annually to the Low Level Waste Repository (LLWR) at Drigg in Cumbria has fallen by 300 per cent over the past 10 years.

Price signals

In principle, the market for selling radioactive waste management services is no different to any other business. The traditional commercial model for selling goods and services involves setting a price based on recovery of the company's fixed costs, variable costs, and sales and marketing costs plus a profit margin. Internal or virtual markets that operate inside organisations usually work in much the same way except there are no sales and marketing costs or profit margins added. Different parts of the same organisation trade with each other on the understanding that neither will generate a profit for their particular business group – an arrangement known as inter-trading.

The internal market for radioactive waste management services is operated today by the Nuclear Decommissioning Authority (NDA). The NDA is vertically integrated, meaning that it supplies waste management services to itself and – in theory at least – they ought to be cheaper than buying in nuclear waste services from an outside company if they were available on the open market. Prices for waste management ought to be the cheapest possible because the service is based on simple cost recovery with no marketing costs and no profit mark-up added.

The problem is that internal markets are rarely competitive, especially in the public sector. They lack any serious outside competition and competition is normally essential to drive down prices. Over the past five years, estimates of the NDA's clean-up costs have escalated on average by around nine per cent each year. This means that the cost of waste management services – the internal market price for dealing with waste – must also have escalated by around nine per cent annually because waste management costs are always a fixed proportion of the NDA's total liability costs. (The NDA's 2006/7 accounts show a nearly constant waste management cost segment ranging from 27 per cent to 30 per cent over the past five years.) The overall picture is that the NDA's £22 billion lifetime cost for managing the 478,000 cubic metres of intermediate- and high-level waste forecast by the Committee on Radioactive Waste Management (CoRWM), implies a levelised unit cost of some £46,000 per cubic metre of waste. These costs are basically for treating and storing radioactive wastes that will arise from the NDA's nuclear decommissioning programme. The cost is driven by the cost for building and running plants for retrieving raw radioactive waste from hazardous environments, processing and immobilising radioactive waste, packaging treated and conditioned radioactive waste, and for storing the packaged radioactive waste over the long term. If the lifecycle cost of a geological repository is also added – thought to be another £10 billion – then the total lifecycle cost rises to £32 billion, bringing the levelised cost of dealing with CoRWM's projected 478,000 cubic metres of waste to an astonishing £67,000 per cubic metre.

For comparison, the price for disposal of low-level waste at the NDA's Low Level Waste Repository (LLWR) at Drigg in Cumbria is only around £2,000 per cubic metre. As a rule of thumb, the price for dealing with intermediate- and high-level waste seems to be about 34 times more expensive than for low-level waste, assuming an internal market operating on a simple cost recovery basis.

Officially there is no truly commercial international market for the disposal of intermediate- and high-level nuclear waste. In Britain, the bulk import and export of radioactive waste was banned under the July 1995 White Paper *Review of Radioactive Waste Management Policy: Final Conclusions*. Instead each country is normally responsible for disposing of its own radioactive waste under the self-sufficiency principle of environmental management, requiring that most waste should be treated or disposed of within the region in which it is produced.

But unofficially countries do trade in small amounts of waste with Britain. These trades take place at what economists call the margin, in which foreign energy utility companies pay only the cost of providing some additional space for commercial waste in the British government's yet-to-be-built geological disposal facility for historic legacy decommissioning wastes. This marginal price gives an important commercial signal of the true market value of a radioactive waste disposal facility. Some insight into the marginal price of intermediate-level waste disposal was given for the first time in the government's detailed 70-page report, *Consultation Paper on Proposals for Intermediate Level Radioactive Waste Substitution*, published in January 2004.

Since 1976 spent fuel reprocessing contracts between Britain and nuclear utility companies in Europe and Japan have required the repatriation of radioactive wastes back to their home country, to avoid Sellafield becoming a 'nuclear dustbin'. However the British government offers an optional waste substitution service – for a price. Waste substitution is the practice of allowing disposal in the UK of foreign-owned intermediate-level radioactive wastes, that have arisen from the reprocessing of foreign spent nuclear fuel at Sellafield, in exchange for shipping a radiologically equivalent but physically smaller volume of high-level waste for return back to the overseas reprocessing customers. The advantage for foreign utilities is that they do not have to worry about constructing intermediate-level waste storage and disposal facilities in their own country, avoiding the high economic cost and political controversy of finding a disposal site. Not surprisingly, over 90 per cent of the 325 organisations that responded to the government's 2004 consultation enthusiastically supported waste substitution. The Department of Trade and Industry officially approved waste substitution via a Parliamentary Statement on 13th December 2004. The NDA subsequently gave Sellafield operational approval for implementation of waste substitution to begin on 27th September 2006. The substitution consultation document explained that 6,480 drums containing 3,240 cubic metres of foreign-owned intermediate-level waste would be kept in the UK – a volume roughly equivalent to four medium-sized British houses. The approximate cost of disposal in a UK repository was estimated to be £87 million but the NDA would charge overseas utility customers a commercial fee of £650 million, delivering a net profit of £563 million (in 2003 prices) – a whopping 647 per cent profit margin. The apparent willingness of overseas utilities to pay a very substantial premium gives an important signal of the true market price for radioactive waste disposal capacity in a British underground repository facility. The foreign utility companies appear to be paying a levelised unit disposal cost of some £201,000 per cubic metre of intermediate-level waste. This would value a commercial deep repository for dealing with all of CoRWM's projected 478,000 cubic metres of nuclear waste as worth around £96 billion if it operated on a fully commercial basis – roughly ten times the £10 billion total lifecycle cost of siting, building, operating and eventually closing a deep waste repository.

British policy of making the polluter pay – in this case overseas utility companies having their spent fuel reprocessed in the UK – means that polluters should quite rightly bear the full costs of their pollution, rather than avoid them. The important thing to remember is that these disposal prices and profit margins are what commercial utilities are willing to pay, not what they actually cost. Nobody is twisting their corporate arms. The utilities could, after all, simply take back their intermediate-level waste and dispose of it themselves. But they don't of course, because Britain offers a relatively good deal for nuclear waste disposal – a very hard to find service, priced at a level that makes good money for the British economy, that foreign utilities can afford to pay.

Paying their full share

The price of waste disposal in a geological repository has become more commercially important with the publication of the government's *White Paper on Nuclear Power* published in January 2008. As a pre-condition for allowing the construction of a new generation of nuclear power stations in Britain, the government decided that energy utility companies must meet their full share of the costs for nuclear waste management and disposal. According to the White Paper, energy companies have indicated that they would be prepared to pay a significant risk premium, over and above the expected costs of disposing of waste, in return for having the certainty of a fixed upper price.

In plain language, the energy companies want fixed price caps on nuclear waste disposal; an understandable position given that the Nuclear Decommissioning Authority's (NDA's) waste management cost forecasts have escalated by nine per cent annually in recent years. Because the NDA is already charging foreign nuclear utilities a premium of 647 per cent profit margin for disposal of substituted intermediate-level wastes, then logically this market premium should be the disposal pricing benchmark for British nuclear utility investors too. Commercially speaking, it is hard to justify charging British utility customers a lower price for geological disposal than overseas utility customers paying for disposal space in the same repository. It would also risk accusations of giving preferential state aid subsidies to nuclear energy utilities investing in Britain, that are potentially illegal under European state aid competition law.

The issue of what utilities should commercially pay as their fair contribution towards the full share of the costs of a repository is controversial because the wastes produced from new nuclear reactor build could have a significant impact on the overall scale of a geological repository. CoRWM's July 2006 report, *Managing our Radioactive Waste Safely*, warned Ministers that the greatest impact on the total radioactive inventory of a nuclear waste repository – the total amount of radioactivity contained at the disposal site – would be from a future programme of new nuclear reactor build. Assuming that 10 new nuclear reactor units were built in Britain, CoRWM estimated that the total volume of waste in a repository would increase by about eight per cent (some 41,000 cubic metres comprising an extra 9,000 cubic metres of intermediate-level waste and 32,000 cubic metres of spent fuel waste) but the total radioactivity in the repository would increase by 300 per cent. Ten reactor units is a sensible forecast because this number would be needed to replace the 9 GWe of nuclear capacity expected to be lost from retirement of Britain's Magnox and AGR nuclear power station fleet over the next 15 years.

Assuming that British utilities would pay the same £201,000 per cubic metre disposal price tag as overseas utilities, then the price of waste disposal for a new build programme would be around £8.2 billion. On the other hand, if the utilities paid only the NDA's internal market rate of £46,000 per cubic metre, the minimum to recover its present waste management costs, then the price of waste disposal from a new nuclear build programme would fall to £1.9 billion. In fact the expansion of a repository to accommodate new build waste might prove to be quite cheap because of the economies of scale normally achieved from scaling up industrial plant capacity. The 'six-tenths rule' is often used in the process indus-try as a general guide to calculating the extra costs of a larger plant. If the cost price of a plant '£P1' is known at capacity 'C1', then the cost price of a new plant '£P2' of capacity 'C2' is given by $£P2 = £P1 \times (C2/C1)^{0.6}$. Using the six-tenths rule, increasing the repository size from CoRWM's 478,000 cubic metre base case up to 519,000 cubic metres to accommodate an extra 41,000 cubic metres of new build waste, would probably increase repository costs by only around five per cent. Because the total lifecycle cost of a repository is thought to be £10 billion, the price of extra space for new nuclear build waste ought to be around £500 million. This would bring the marginal cost of disposal of new build waste in an expanded repository down to a rock bottom price of £12,200 per cubic metre of waste.

The extra repository space needed for new reactor build might cost the NDA as little as £500 million, but could be worth up to £8.2 billion commercially. British nuclear utility companies would be well advised to lobby for disposal prices fixed towards the lower £500 million valua-tion, perhaps adding a fairly generous 100 per cent market premium to reflect the risk of repos-itory cost escalation borne by the NDA. Meanwhile taxpayers and HM Treasury might want to press for the full £8.2 billion marginal valuation that foreign nuclear utility companies appear willing to pay for geological disposal of substituted wastes. The problem is that unfortunately this fully commercial price would make disposal far too expensive, killing the prospects of any new nuclear build programme in Britain. The £8.2 billion waste disposal cost, spread across 10 new reactors, amounts to £820 million per reactor, equivalent to 41 per cent of each reactor's expected £2 billion capital cost. Business models for nuclear generation assume back end costs of only five per cent for decommissioning and waste management. As a result, the NDA may need to fix repository waste disposal prices in the range from £500 million to £1,000 million (£50 million to £100 million per new reactor) for new build to remain economically viable.

The bottom line is that nuclear energy utilities probably need fixed waste disposal 'prices' for repository disposal capped somewhere in the range from £12,200 to £24,400 per cubic metre, the NDA's marginal cost of the extra repository space is £12,200 per cubic metre, the full cost of managing the NDA's own wastes is nearer to £67,000 per cubic metre, and the commercial 'value' of the repository asset could approach £201,000 per cubic metre if operated as a fully private sector venture. If the price signals from foreign waste substitution contracts truly reflect the market's valuation of repository space, then the government may need to cap the margin-al costs of waste disposal space at around 6 to 12 per cent of their full commercial value to make new nuclear stations a viable investment. The counterargument is that waste substitution customers are simply buying an ILW to HLW conversion service, not storage space in a British repository. But with an apparent market premium of 647 per cent, that view is probably naïve. The commercial signal is that ILW repository space is genuinely valuable to foreign utilities.

Just as high street retailers offer discounts to customers, it is difficult to say whether or not the price of repository space charged to utilities will be subsidised by the government to incentivise new nuclear build. British utilities might not pay as much as foreign utilities for disposing of waste in the UK, but they would still be paying enough to cover their share of the basic cost for building and running the repository. Both foreign and British utilities would definitely be covering the government's minimum costs. So far, so good. But the economically tricky debate is whether or not the NDA should charge foreign utility customers higher profit margins than British utility customers for waste disposal, and whether any difference in these profit margins represents a *de facto* subsidy to British utilities. A subsidy is a form of financial assistance generally paid by government to keep prices artificially below what they would be in a normally functioning liberalised market. The assistance in this case would be an artificially low market price for disposing of intermediate-level and spent fuel waste from new nuclear power stations. The government is likely to pick a fixed unit price for waste disposal towards the lower end of estimates because if it charges utility companies too much then the economic case for new nuclear build falls apart. Because the role of the NDA is to maximise public revenue from its commercial operations then – in theory at least – the NDA should always try to maximise its profit margins by selling repository space to the highest bidder. This would ultimately mean selling space to foreign utilities in preference to British utilities who would probably pay less. In economic terms, by selling to British utilities the NDA pays an opportunity cost because the NDA loses the opportunity to sell the repository space to the higher bidder. If there is any major difference in profit margins then the opportunity cost paid by the NDA might indeed look very much like a state subsidy for new nuclear reactor build. In plain language, *eBay*-savvy British taxpayers might want to question the government's motivation for selling something for less than it is really worth.

Compensating host communities

Nuclear siting is a high stakes game for both governments and local communities. The practical prospects for a revival of nuclear energy in Britain may well crucially depend on finding a site for a geological repository to dispose of spent fuel and decommissioning wastes. The local community hosting the repository will inevitably play a pivotal role in deciding whether Britain embarks on a major new nuclear build programme or retreats from nuclear power completely. This places a considerable degree of political and market power in the hands of any local communities who might decide to volunteer to host a repository site.

The Committee on Radioactive Waste Management's (CoRWM's) recommendation to Ministers for geological disposal was not price sensitive. CoRWM compared the situation to car buying, noting that cost may be a very important criterion when buying a new car, but if all the cars under consideration cost much the same, then other criteria become more important as discriminators. CoRWM's report to Ministers did not provide cost estimates for a geological repository but referenced NIREX's September 2005 *Summary Note for CoRWM on Cost Estimates for CoRWM Option 7 (Deep Geological Disposal) and Option 9 (Phased Deep Geological Disposal)*. The NIREX report forecast the initial cost of siting and constructing a geological repository up to the point of first waste emplacement to be £3.5 billion with a total whole lifecycle cost of £10 billion.

CoRWM's Chair, Professor Gordon MacKerron, a highly regarded energy economist, neatly summarised the expected range of lifecycle costs as between £10 billion and £18 billion in a technical paper for the Committee, *Note on Costs* (CoRWM Document 1564), published on 21st February 2006. CoRWM's Chairman pointed out that as no commercial waste management facility for higher activity wastes had been constructed anywhere in the world, there was no reliable historical guide to costs likely to be incurred in the UK. Costing waste management facilities with any degree of accuracy relies on having a detailed facility design at a specific disposal site location. Because repository design is very closely linked to the specific geology of a site, it would be difficult to fully determine costs until final siting decisions were taken by the government and the Nuclear Decommissioning Authority (NDA). These uncertainties mean that the risks of significant cost escalation are high. Nevertheless both NIREX and CoRWM were in broad agreement that the total lifecycle cost of siting, building, operating and closing a geological repository would likely be around £10 billion to £11 billion as a central estimate (neither too pessimistic nor too optimistic).

An approximate breakdown of the cost structure suggested by NIREX for development of a geological repository is roughly £1 billion (10 per cent) for site investigation and characterisation, £2.5 billion (25 per cent) for repository development and construction up to the point of first waste emplacement, £3.6 billion (36 per cent) for operation of the repository, £2 billion (20 per cent) for expansion of the repository to accommodate high-level waste, spent fuel, plutonium and uranium, £0.3 billion (3 per cent) for repository closure, and around £0.7 billion (7 per cent) in sunk costs and research already undertaken by NIREX.

The development of a geological repository for nuclear waste crucially hinges on whether any local community will actually come forward and volunteer to host a repository site. In democratic countries, communities are generally powerful enough to delay or stop the development of unwanted projects. The basic requirement for acceptance is that towns must be better off with the nuclear repository than without it, and this means compensating the host community in some way. CoRWM recommended that the government should offer community benefit packages such as funding investment in better roads, motorways, schools, hospitals, universities, and affordable housing. But what they boil down to is money. And lots of it.

Early negotiations with the government have been led by the Local Government Association's Nuclear Legacy Advisory Forum (NuLeAF). Perhaps mindful of declining nuclear employment, NuLeAF has pressed the government for a benefits package that is both ambitious and transformational so that it will have a significant and lasting effect on the host area – almost certainly one in which a nuclear site is already located. In fact, community benefits packages are already a common feature of planning permissions agreed between civil developers and cash-strapped local authorities, as an essential sweetener to help fund local housing and infrastructure investment. These packages, known as Section 106 Agreements under the Town and County Planning Act 1990, are normally geared towards some negotiated fixed percentage of the total value of the development. A study of funding levels by the Audit Commission, *Securing Community Benefits through the Planning Process*, published in August 2006, found that community benefits packages typically did not exceed 10 per cent of the value of the development and were often much less. Negotiated packages were generally higher in southern England where there was competition amongst developers for access to land, but lower in northern England because councils were concerned that attempting to squeeze funding from developers might deter economic investment or encourage it to take place in a neighbouring authority instead.

The 10 per cent gearing factor may prove to be an important benchmark for assessing the level of benefits that a community might reasonably expect for agreeing to host a national geological repository for nuclear waste. Because the development value of a British nuclear repository in the market place is worth around £96 billion when charging fully commercial waste disposal rates, the community benefits package might be worth as high as £9.6 billion. On the other hand, if the benefits package is geared only to the £3.5 billion investment cost of siting and constructing a nuclear repository up to the point of first waste emplacement, the community benefits package might be worth only £350 million. Both of these valuations are unrealistic. £9.6 billion is too high for the taxpayer to afford, pushing the lifecycle cost of a repository up to the £20 billion mark. Conversely £350 million is probably too low to offer any real incentive for local communities to accept the waste, as the money is unlikely to achieve the desired ambitious and transformational effect on the local economy. The middle ground appears to be a community benefit package worth around £1 billion geared to the expected £10 billion whole lifecycle cost of a geological repository.

But local residents expecting to see some of the money in their own bank accounts are likely to be disappointed. Rather than pay lump sums to individual residents or offer council tax rebates and other tax breaks, NuLeAF has proposed that the cash is managed by the local authority instead with some of the money going towards an intergeneration trust fund that will have a lasting beneficial effect on the area.

Bidding strategies

The relative strength of the bargaining position of any local authority competing to host a repository will depend on how many other authorities might also be willing to host the same repository. This boils down to a sales process, where what is being sold is the exclusive rights to site a geological repository, for a price determined by the size of the community benefit package. The government, as the sole buyer, needs to attract as many potential sellers as possible. If only one willing local community comes forward, that community will have considerable market power and can more or less dictate its own selling terms. On the other hand competition from just one extra seller can significantly reduce the price that the government will have to pay.

It is important to appreciate that the buying psychology for purchasing a repository site is completely different when compared with the situation of buying a site for a new nuclear power station. When selling government-owned land for building a new nuclear power station, the government must encourage energy utilities to compete with each other, driving-up the sale price of the development land for new nuclear build as far as possible. But when buying a site to host its own repository, the government must encourage as many sellers as possible to offer their sites up for sale, driving down the price to the lowest possible level. This situation, where many sellers compete for the business of one buyer, is known as a reverse auction in game theory. The dynamics of the reverse auction has led to fears of a downward bidding war developing between less well-off communities in economically deprived rural areas tempted to host such facilities. Commercial experience with reverse auctions in the US manufacturing sector, pioneered by auction firms FreeMarkets and Ariba, were found to reduce wholesale prices by 20 to 40 per cent. The fear is that community benefits packages paid out by government will be similarly cut through a siting competition process.

The Conservative government's July 1995 *Review of Radioactive Waste Management Policy: Final Conclusions* White Paper stated that 30 per cent of the British mainland was considered to offer geological and hydrogeological potential for repository development. In June 2005 NIREX published its landmark report, *Review of 1987-1991 Site Selection for an ILW/LLW Repository*, containing a previously secret list of 537 sites that it had considered during the 1980s as potential locations for building a national repository. During the NIREX siting exercise there was generally no contact with land owners, so there was little or no awareness that their land had been identified. After completing desk-based studies, NIREX concluded that 39 sites were considered suitable on a geological basis, and nine sites were eventually short-listed as the most geologically promising: Sandray, Fuday, Dounreay and Altnabreac in Scotland, Sellafield in Cumbria, Killingholme in Humberside, Stanford in Norfolk, and Bradwell and Potton Island in Essex. Although NIREX was quick to reassure people that the 2005 siting report was only of historic interest, NuLeAF recognised that some of the locations could potentially be considered again as volunteers in any new siting process. After all, the original NIREX site selection team, now part of the NDA, contained some of the best technical experts in Britain and their expert judgements are still likely to remain valid today. But crucially the shortlisting process was skewed because NIREX was not granted compulsory purchase powers to enable it to acquire a site for development of a repository. NIREX was restricted principally to considering sites that were already owned by government or by the nuclear industry. The NIREX report is good evidence that there ought to be a sufficient pool of sites technically capable of hosting a repository and in principle that several different communities might be willing to compete for benefits packages offered by the government.

However, giving an early warning sign of potential trouble ahead, on 25th June 2007 the newly elected Scottish National Party (SNP) devolved government in Scotland formally withdrew from the UK government's repository siting process, *Managing Radioactive Waste Safely*. Scotland opted for storage instead. Britain's future nuclear waste repository will now most likely be built in England or Wales unless there is a change of government policy in Scotland. The withdrawal of Scotland, losing four out of the nine UK locations previously regarded as amongst the most promising, is also likely to have a significant economic impact, driving up the price of the community benefits package as the remaining pool of available sites becomes much smaller.

The price of a repository site, expressed as the size of the negotiated community benefits package, may also be affected by various situational factors that have a bearing on what compensation may be appropriate. For example, there is general consensus within local government that under the proximity principle and the self sufficiency principle, each local authority should be responsible for managing radioactive wastes generated by their own nearby nuclear facilities. The logic is that the local communities who have financially benefited from nuclear employment should shoulder some moral responsibility for managing the nuclear wastes produced locally.

In the United States this has led to the emergence of two-tier pricing structures for the disposal of some low-level radioactive wastes. Waste imported from outside states are charged a higher price for disposal than waste generated within the state boundary, or in practice within a small coalition of politically aligned groups of states who have signed up to waste compact agreements together. States inside the compact pay lower prices than States outside the compact, and may even reject low-level radioactive wastes from non-compact members.

British community benefits packages might be structured in a similar way, paying more compensation for wastes imported into the county from other parts of Britain and less compensation for wastes already existing within the county. By far the largest proportion of nuclear waste is already located at the Sellafield nuclear plant in Cumbria where around 60 per cent of all higher activity waste destined for a deep repository will be generated. If a national repository were sited in Cumbria – still regarded by many as the front-runner despite the failure of the NIREX 1997 public inquiry – then the government might need to pay more community benefit for the 40 per cent of waste that would be imported into the county but less benefit (or maybe even no benefit at all) for the 60 per cent of the UK's waste already situated there. On the other hand a new entrant into the nuclear siting market, for example a virgin local community having no previous nuclear history who volunteered to host a national repository site for economic reasons, might feel perfectly entitled to claim substantially more community benefit than Cumbria.

By the same token, host communities are likely to demand extra compensation for hosting the substantially increased radioactive inventory of spent fuel waste from any new nuclear power programme in Britain. The issue of compensation for new build wastes remains tremendously sensitive. Early indications are that it is potentially a deal-breaker even for pro-nuclear communities. The size of the additional compensation package expected for new build wastes is problematic because expanding a repository might be quite cheap – only £500 million using the six-tenths rule – yet communities will expect a much higher pay-off than the benchmark 10 per cent compensation gearing under Section 106 planning agreements. From a local community perspective it hardly seems worth the trouble of accepting new build waste, tripling the radioactive hazard in the repository, for only an extra £50 million in compensation. Some upward negotiation seems highly likely as it is in the best interests of nuclear utility companies to have a disposal route for their spent reactor fuel available to them.

Compensating Drigg

The first litmus test of the bargaining power of British local communities to secure compensation for nuclear waste disposal was fought and won at Drigg in Cumbria.

Drigg is the site of Britain's only disposal facility for low-level nuclear waste, a 50-year-old repository site that opened in 1959, now owned by the government's Nuclear Decommissioning Authority (NDA). Between 2005 and 2007 a Mexican standoff occurred in which the local planning authority Cumbria County Council, in coalition with Copeland Borough Council and Drigg & Carleton Parish Council, had together effectively blocked planning permission for an urgently-needed expansion of the Drigg repository. All of Drigg's historic disposal trenches and vaults had been completely filled with low-level nuclear waste. Yet despite at least £10 million invested by the government in developing a nuclear safety case study running to over 3,000 pages, the radiological disposal capacity of the site remained unknown. This was particularly worrying because the radiological capacity is the total amount of radioactive waste that can safely be buried at Drigg without breaching radiation dose limits or risk targets in the future. A complex regulatory review by the Environment Agency had cost over £1 million alone. The Environment Agency had first flagged the radiological capacity problem in a detailed 226-page consultation package comprising an *Explanatory Document to assist public consultation on proposals for the future regulation of disposals of radioactive waste on/from the Low-Level Waste Repository at Drigg, Cumbria operated by British Nuclear Group Sellafield Ltd* and an accompanying *Assessment of BNFL's 2002 Environmental Safety Cases for the Low-Level Radioactive Waste Repository at Drigg*, both published in June 2005. The Environment Agency's conclusions released in February 2006 were explained in a comprehensive 104-page Decision Document on *Future Regulation of Disposals of Radioactive Waste at the Low-Level Radioactive Waste Repository at Drigg, Cumbria*. The Agency decided not to authorise any further waste disposals until Cumbria County Council had approved planning permission for construction of a new disposal vault within the Drigg site, putting Cumbria County Council firmly in the driving seat.

Without disposal at Drigg, the NDA's nuclear decommissioning programme risked grinding to a halt, potentially causing waste to pile up in temporary storage areas on UK nuclear sites or more likely having to suspend waste-generating decommissioning work. The NDA blinked first.

After a highly sensitive year-long negotiation between Cumbria and the NDA and HM Treasury, on 11th January 2008 the NDA announced the formation of a £22 million West Cumbria Community Fund, the first such nuclear community benefits fund of its kind in Britain. The fund was structured to provide an initial endowment of £10 million with further annual payments £1.5 million for each year the repository remained open, likely to be around eight years. Cumbria County Council had given planning permission for storage of 110,000 cubic metres of low-level waste in Vault 9. The new storage vault is expected to receive 700 ISO waste containers annually, and can accommodate 5,500 ISO containers before it is filled up after about eight to ten years.

In 1998 the late Professor Sir John Knill, a former chairman of the government's Radioactive Waste Management Advisory Committee (RWMAC), pointed out that in the future new repositories would probably need to operate as retrievable stores in the first instance. The concept of retrievability blurs the line between disposal and storage. The problem of how to reduce future radiation doses from Drigg whilst at the same time increasing its disposal capacity was partially resolved by effectively reclassifying Drigg as a long-term interim storage facility rather than a permanent disposal site. This compromise solution was possible because the Drigg repository can be regarded as two sites in one. 'Old Drigg' consists of a series of seven disposal trenches operated between 1959 and 1995. Radioactive wastes were simply tumble-tipped into the trenches and permanently covered over with no intention to retrieve the buried wastes. 'New Drigg' is rather different and has many of the characteristics of a waste storage facility rather than a disposal site. Since 1995 low-level waste has been containerised in ISO containers used for international freight haulage and then transported via road to a surface storage vault at Drigg. The ISO containers are stacked in a large open-plan concrete area resembling a sea freight storage terminal. In principle these ISO containers could all be retrieved if necessary. Cumbria County Council deliberately factored this retrievability requirement into the new planning permission granted for the expansion of Drigg.

Unfortunately the Achilles heel of the Drigg site is that it is a surface repository situated on the coast, making the site potentially vulnerable to the long-term effects of climate change. The Environment Agency had forecast that under some climate scenarios, Drigg might be completely destroyed by a possible rise in the coastal sea level of the Irish Sea perhaps within a timeframe as soon as 500 years, although of course this was not certain to occur. Drigg's retrievability requirement now means that there is a strong likelihood of the newly stored wastes, and possibly some of the older wastes, eventually being recovered to an alternative disposal location – the main contender being shared room space inside a national geological repository facility.

From a business perspective, perhaps the most obvious solution for increasing disposal capacity at Drigg would be to selectively retrieve and repackage some known historic disposals of uranium, radium and thorium wastes that were tumble-tipped into the Drigg trenches in the 1970s and 1980s. At present these specific disposals significantly increase the overall risk profile of the Drigg site by about a factor of 10. Selective remediation of some hot spots could be the best strategy to reduce risks and allow an increase in disposal capacity. The NDA could justify the small increase in risk from construction of new vault capacity against an equivalent reduction in risk from partial remediation of the trenches, targeted against key nuclides at a few specific locations. Information would be needed on possible intervention options for the trenches, how much they would reduce risk, how much they would cost and whether or not this investment would represent best value for money for the NDA or would be disproportionate to the potential benefits gained from making extra disposal capacity available at Drigg. In practice the incremental cost of trench remediation would almost certainly be lower than the total cost of siting and developing another low-level radioactive waste repository elsewhere in the UK – it is usually much cheaper to expand an existing repository than to build a new one.

The size of the £22 million community benefits package negotiated for Drigg has confirmed some important compensation principles for a deep nuclear waste repository. Firstly, the size of the benefits package has been geared to the expected 10 per cent of the value of the development. Waste disposal at Drigg costs £2,000 per cubic metre of low-level waste, implying that the value of the new 110,000 cubic metre storage capacity is £220 million. Secondly, compensation has been paid even though 60 per cent of the waste is generated locally at the neighbouring Sellafield nuclear plant. The notion that taking disposal responsibility for home-grown waste might not be compensated, or compensated to a lesser extent by government, does not seem to have been borne out. Thirdly, the main financial beneficiary seems to be the 69,000 residents of Copeland Borough Council rather than the 300 villagers of Drigg & Carleton Parish Council. Of the £22 million benefits package, less then two per cent, only £50,000 per year (£400,000 in total spread over eight years) will be ring-fenced specifically for the village of Drigg, equivalent to just £167 per person annually – a worryingly low incentive that might make other small communities think twice before volunteering their village for hosting a deep waste repository. But for Copeland Borough Council it is a very good eight-year deal, worth more than half of the Council's £41 million annual income in 2007. Clearly nuclear benefits packages have some potential to divide community opinion.

Hedging bets on waste storage

The many complicating situational factors that affect geological repository bidding strategies – variations in the technical suitability of the volunteered sites, the degree of nuclear waste already existing in a county, any previous nuclear history, attitudes towards accommodating waste from new nuclear build, and the relative strength and prosperity of the local economy – mean that different communities competing with each other to host a repository will each have different expectations of the community benefits package that they would be willing to accept. These are called independent private valuations (IPVs) by game theorists, although they are not fully independent because some collusion is likely between communities. For example, it makes sense for communities to get together and agree beforehand the minimum deal from government that any of them would be prepared to accept. Moreover, realistically the pool of available bidders is not likely to be very large, partly because nuclear repositories are unpopular with local communities anyway and partly because the government will be obliged to adopt some pre-qualification process, screening out sites that are either technically too difficult, geologically unsuitable, or uncomfortably close to other potentially valuable resources such as coal and oil deposits or groundwater aquifers.

Although individual bidding strategies are likely to be complex, one thing is certain: because the objective of the government is to use competition to drive down the overall price of benefits packages, there comes a point when bidders will drop out leading to the final minimum value that any community is prepared to accept. Yet there are fears in government that even this minimum walk-away price might still prove too high for taxpayers and HM Treasury to bear. If communities want too much money they could force the government into a waste storage policy by default, maintaining the present *status quo*. Waste stores are cheaper to build and far less controversial than repositories. With a working lifetime of 100 years, as few as 30 modern waste stores similar to the £100 million Encapsulated Product Store 2 (EPS2) store recently built at Sellafield, or the EPS3 store currently under construction, could accommodate all of Britain's 478,000 cubic metres of waste forecast by CoRWM. The total capital cost would be near £3 billion but with economies of scale from building a large number of identical stores, the cost might drop to perhaps as low as £2 billion. From an economic and practical standpoint storage remains an attractive fallback position for the government.

Scotland quickly withdrew from deep disposal and opted for storage even before the British government's fledgling repository site selection consultation process had got off the ground in June 2007. This point is not lost on some local authorities near existing nuclear installations who have been pressing the government behind the scenes for benefits packages, irrespective of whether wastes remain stored on nuclear sites or are disposed of in a future geological repository. Despite CoRWM's recommendation for a national repository to be built, it seems that at least some enlightened players in local government are hedging their bets against the possibility that storage prevails over deep disposal.

A similar story is currently being played out in America, where the prospects for opening the Yucca Mountain repository in Nevada for commercial spent nuclear fuel look increasingly uncertain. If America significantly expands its low carbon nuclear energy capability under President George W Bush's Global Nuclear Energy Partnership (GNEP), then storage and reprocessing of spent nuclear fuel become more probable in the United States rather than disposal at Yucca Mountain.

However what works in America does not always work in Britain. Policymakers need to exercise caution with applying US solutions to the UK, not least because of cultural differences. Culturally, Americans tend to be more motivated by money than Europeans. As Robert Day explains in his 2004 book *Working the American Way – How to communicate successfully with Americans at work*, US attitudes towards money and capitalism are genuinely different to the broadly socialist governments of Britain and Europe. From a cultural standpoint, Americans are more flexible and pragmatic, willing to accept financial benefits and trade-offs that British people might not always be willing to make.

Although deep disposal is generally presented by the British government, and CoRWM, as the best technical solution preferred by nuclear scientists, this picture is not completely true. At least some mainstream nuclear engineers remain privately sceptical about deep disposal and are more inclined towards spent fuel reprocessing and storage as the optimum solution – or at least designing a deep repository to serve as a fully retrievable underground store in the first instance. CoRWM recommended early closure of a geological repository, soon after it had been fully loaded with waste, but recommended that the host community should have the final say on whether closure should be delayed and the nuclear waste made potentially retrievable. Storage also has the key advantage that sites are automatically self-selecting and so do not require any politically divisive site-selection process to decide where wastes must be located. Moreover long-term storage does not foreclose any options for alternative management of the radioactive wastes that may be possible in the future when new waste treatment and immobilisation technologies will inevitably become available. Research commissioned by British Nuclear Fuels plc (BNFL) from the Institute of Nanotechnology (IoN) signalled several potentially interesting developments. The Institute's 2003 report, *A Brief Study on Trends in Nanotechnology in Relation to its Possible Impact on Nuclear Decommissioning*, flagged the possibility of dendrimer nanomaterials that could recognise low levels of plutonium and uranium in the environment and selectively adsorb them, for example immobilising any contamination that might leak from a waste repository.

One of the leading concepts for storage as a serious alternative to deep disposal was presented to CoRWM members by British Nuclear Group (BNG), the highly respected decommissioning business subsidiary of BNFL. On 12th June 2005 *The Independent* reported that BNG had developed a conceptual design for a series of gently sloping dome-shaped national storage facilities, having a planned lifetime of 1,000 years, to be constructed at Sellafield, carefully landscaped and buried just under the surface of the ground. This catenary arch dome storage concept was fast gaining political support within Whitehall. Developed by a BNG design team led by a former Nuclear Installations Inspectorate regulator, the 1,000-year storage plan was a potential repository-killer. It was to all intents and purposes a workable 'Plan B' solution if no repository site was forthcoming. The basic technical details were revealed in a favourable assessment report commissioned by CoRWM, *Discussion paper on the implementability of radioactive waste management options* (CoRWM document number 1167), published in July 2005. In principle the 1,000-year store was essentially a much larger version of the existing EPS2 store at Sellafield. The size of the store would be scaled up to accommodate wastes received from many nuclear sites in the UK, with different types of waste segregated into different modular storage zones or indeed in entirely separate mounded stores co-located together.

The detailed design of the 1,000-year store was somewhat different to EPS2 involving a gentle mounded arch store design some four times larger than the EPS2 store, constructed using compressed concrete. BNG removed most of the life-limiting vulnerable steelwork systems from the existing EPS2 store design, to develop a 1,000-year store concept that did not contain any metal reinforcing that would otherwise be prone to corrosion over very long timeframes. The presence of steel reinforcement within modern concrete structures is their main Achilles' heel. But in a catenary arch dome, steel is not needed because geometry and gravity achieve the necessary compression structure and strength.

The nuclear industry has only around 60 years experience of operating storage facilities for radioactive wastes but a long-term store would need to operate for much longer periods up to 1,000 years. As yet there is relatively little scientific and engineering experience of constructing technically advanced facilities intended to operate much longer than 50 to 100 years. Worldwide, new nuclear power stations are probably the most technically advanced long-lived structures, which have planned lifetimes of around 60 years. Nevertheless some civil engineers argue that 1,000 years is not a prohibitive nor a critical duration over which to assure the efficiency of materials and structures made from concrete. The most impressive evidence of the durability of concrete structures remains the dome of the Pantheon in Rome which was constructed in 150 AD and has never required significant restoration. The dome was cast using a rough grout similar to modern cement. BNG's 1,000-year store concept is based on a mounded store design using similar compressed concrete construction techniques to the Pantheon.

BNG argued that the store would be suitable for all types of radioactive wastes examined by CoRWM without the need for refurbishment every 100 years required by other storage designs. Such a store would effectively become a mausoleum requiring perpetual guardianship by government. However the engineering design life of the store may not be the most important factor determining the feasibility of the store from a technical perspective. The most critical parameter may be the lifetime of the radioactive waste drums and their stability and resilience to corrosion, temperature and humidity. It is foreseeable that at least some waste drums would eventually degrade, requiring either repackaging (probably using a simple overpacking arrangement to minimise handling of the waste) or if this was not possible, recovery of the old waste drum succeeded by treatment and reworking of the waste into a new waste drum container. At present many wastes are contained within stainless steel waste drums of various types. However, stainless steel is a relatively modern material first introduced around 1910. Its corrosion resistance and overall resilience to degradation over long periods much greater than 100 years is not known with certainty although radioactive waste packaging standards specified by NIREX and the Nuclear Decommissioning Authority (NDA) are intended to ensure drums of waste are safely retrievable for periods of up to 300 years.

In contrast, during the early 1990s some 45-year-old intermediate-level waste packages originating from Sir John Cockcroft's early experiments at UKAEA Harwell in the 1940s were found to have almost completely disintegrated inside their concrete storage vaults at the B462 waste handling complex. The Harwell vault stores have now been completely refurbished to modern standards and a programme of recovery and repackaging of the wastes has taken place. Nevertheless experience at B462 provides some indication of the difficulty of assuring the lifetime of waste drums with certainty.

In 2004 NIREX published a research report, *Corrosion Resistance of Stainless Steel Radioactive Waste Packages*, examining the likely corrosion resistance of stainless steel radioactive waste drums that are intended for disposal in a geological repository. The research, which examined a number of case histories and corrosion mechanisms, suggested that atmospheric corrosion might lead to some surface pitting of the stainless steel waste drums after around 90 years in an industrial environment or around 1,000 years in a rural environment. This would not automatically result in the immediate release of contamination from stored waste drums, but would probably require repackaging of some waste drums during the 1,000-year storage period. Even with the highest quality control during manufacture, premature containment failure of the waste drum must be taken into account in the design of the waste store. In the Swedish and Finnish concepts for the disposal of spent nuclear fuel, retrievability is a design requirement and the copper-steel containers are designed to remain intact for over 10,000 years, although pin hole defects during manufacture may lead to early canister failure within 1,000 to 1,500 years.

The question of whether Britain will adopt a radical 1,000-year nuclear waste storage policy will largely depend on community attitudes towards hosting a geological repository. If no host community comes forward offering a disposal site, or if the price of the community benefits package asked for is too steep for the government to reasonably pay, then storage with spent fuel reprocessing is the most likely outcome. The government's 2008 *White Paper on Nuclear Power* signalled strong support for nuclear energy as a key contribution towards eventually decarbonising the British economy to meet the country's low-carbon energy generation goals. But a waste repository is needed to deliver this vision. Bearing this in mind, there is an important distinction between market demand, which merely means that someone will buy a product, and societal need where the absence of something has such an acute effect that government should intervene to supply it. If expansion of nuclear energy proves essential to fight the technological battle against climate change, then government should – and must – step in to provide waste management facilities that enable continued nuclear energy generation. In the absence of a deep disposal site, 1,000-year storage might just offer the optimum path by combining technical feasibility with least political resistance.

Further Reading

F Barker, *Developing the Implementation Framework: Funding Participation and Enhancing Community Wellbeing*, Nuclear Legacy Advisory Forum, Briefing Paper 5, 2007.

L Bailey, *Responses to CoRWM Questions Regarding the Nirex Viability Report*, CoRWM Document Number 1609, 2006.

A Hooper, *Review of 1987-1991 Site Selection for an ILW/LLW Repository*, NIREX Technical Note 477002, 2005.

S Lesbiral and D Shaw, *Managing Conflict in Facility Siting: An International Comparison*, Edward Elgar Publishing, 2005.

M Crawford and S Wickham, *CoRWM Criteria Discussion Paper: Cost*, Galson Sciences Limited, CoRWM, 2005.

G Varley, D Collier and F Strydom, *Consultation Paper on Proposals for Intermediate Level Radioactive Waste Substitution*, Department of Trade and Industry, 2004.

M Dobson, *A Long Term Management Facility for Nuclear Wastes at the Sellafield Site*, British Nuclear Group, 2004.

The Handling of Timescales in Assessing Post-closure Safety, Nuclear Energy Agency, Organisation for Economic Co-operation and Development, 2004.

C McCutcheon, *Nuclear Reactions: The Politics of Opening a Radioactive Waste Disposal Site*, University of New Mexico Press, 2002.

M Gerrard, *Whose Backyard, Whose Risk: Fear and Fairness in Toxic and Nuclear Waste Siting*, MIT Press, 1994.

Chapter 4

Selling Plutonium: The Market for MOX

Market crash

In 2006 the European nuclear firm Belgonucleaire, the world's second largest producer of plutonium-uranium mixed oxide (MOX) fuel for civil nuclear power stations, effectively went bust. The international market for MOX reactor fuel had collapsed. Belgonucleaire was unable to secure any further orders for its MOX fuel, its sole commercial product, from nuclear energy utility companies worldwide. Despite an excellent 20-year manufacturing track record, with zero failures of its MOX fuel loaded inside nuclear reactors, the small Belgian company established in 1957 and until recently employing 314 people was forced to close its highly efficient MOX factory situated in the picturesque town of Dessel, some 90 kilometres from Brussels. Since 1986 the Dessel MOX plant had regularly produced 39 tonnes of MOX fuel each year destined for the French, German, Swiss, Belgian and Japanese markets. Belgonucleaire's Dessel plant was so efficient that it utilised over 97 per cent of its maximum 40 tonne annual plant capacity.

In stark contrast, six years after its commissioning began in 2001, the Sellafield MOX Plant (SMP), Britain's £490 million flagship MOX facility owned by the Nuclear Decommissioning Authority (NDA), struggled to produce just 2.6 tonnes of MOX fuel elements in the 2006/2007 financial year from an automated plant designed to manufacture 120 tonnes annually. According to the National Audit Office, the original £265 million capital expenditure proposal for SMP approved by the Board of British Nuclear Fuels plc (BNFL) in 1993 envisaged active commissioning of the plant in 1997 with a four-year ramp-up of production reaching maximum capacity by 2001. Plant commissioning was delayed by a complex politically-driven four-year regulatory licensing process and eventually began in 2001. The NDA inherited SMP from BNFL in 2005 as part of a dowry of commercial assets intended to generate revenue for Britain's nuclear clean-up programme.

Writing about SMP in his personal website blog on 8th November 2004, Michael Meacher MP commented: "As Environment Minister at the time, I was unconvinced of the economic viability of the project and resisted it for three years. Unfortunately, the Prime Minister [Tony Blair] chose to override this advice and gave his approval for its go-ahead in 2001."

It had not helped that BNFL applied for a regulatory justification licence only after SMP had been built, presenting regulators with a political *fait accompli*, a situation the Environment Agency was clearly unhappy with. The Agency's *Proposed Decision on the Justification for the Plutonium Commissioning and Full Operation of the Mixed Oxide Fuel Plant*, published in October 1998, commented in its Executive Summary: "The time at which an application is received is crucial to the Agency's involvement in the regulation of new plant. The application for the MOX plant was received after the plant was built and after the capital cost had been incurred. The Agency is dissatisfied that it was unable to consider the full economic case before construction began. It is seeking a change in the legislation to prevent similar situations occurring in the future."

The justification licensing position is analogous to obtaining outline planning permission before construction of a new building. Ignoring sunk costs makes a nonsense of justification decisions based solely on economic criteria. The law was indeed later changed although perhaps not quite in the way the Environment Agency had intended. The Justification of Practices Involving Ionising Radiation Regulations 2004 transferred the Agency's justification decision-making authority to the government's Secretary of State, although the Agency remains a statutory consultee.

Justification decisions are a central component of the environmental licensing of new nuclear plants. Under European safety law, new nuclear plants may not be licensed unless their operation is justified in advance. This means that radioactive discharges from the plant may not be licensed by the regulators unless the benefits to society outweigh any radiation detriments, these detriments being principally small radiation doses to members of the public in the local environment receiving the discharge. Although precise calculations of the projected radiation doses are subject to scientific debate depending upon which particular calculation method is chosen, the broad magnitude of the likely radiation exposure of members of the public and the very low probability of any adverse health effects are well understood. But paradoxically, public health effects are often not the deciding factor in justification decisions. This is because from a radiological protection perspective, public radiation exposure detriments are often very small in comparison with the legal public radiation dose limit of 1,000 microsieverts per year. For example the maximum annual radiation exposure of any member of the public from SMP was estimated to be just two thousandths of a microsievert annually which is 500,000 times lower than the public radiation dose limit.

In reality justification decisions mainly concern the evaluation of benefits to society, which are normally presented in economic terms. Justification decisions therefore often depend on a wider economic analysis of the case for a nuclear plant and how the plant's economic benefits can be offset against perhaps small health effects to a few exposed individuals from the plant's radioactive discharges.

After SMP's justification had been approved by the government in 2001, SMP was commissioned by introducing plutonium into the plant for the first time. This was a key technical and political step marking the point of no return for the government after the plant had officially 'gone live' with plutonium. Having been personally approved by New Labour Prime Minister Tony Blair, the government was now committed to bringing SMP fully online. By 2004 – the year before ownership of the plant was transferred from BNFL to the NDA – the capital cost of SMP had risen to £490 million. The utilisation of the SMP facility, a key measure of its manufacturing efficiency, was just 2.2 per cent in 2007. Production targets for SMP were scaled back by BNFL to 72 tonnes in 2001, and revised downwards again by the NDA in 2006 to a best-case forecast of an ultimate target of around 40 tonnes MOX production per year, the minimum to recover its running costs.

Even without the market collapse, SMP remains hopelessly uneconomic compared with the shutdown Belgian plant. If the NDA continues to bankroll SMP, then British taxpayers realistically stand to lose several billion pounds (on top of the £0.5 billion in sunk costs already spent on building and repairing SMP) funding the shortfall between the cost to produce MOX in SMP and the market price for which it can be sold worldwide.

Fuel pricing signals

The business case for manufacturing plutonium-uranium mixed oxide (MOX) fuel exploits the recyclability of plutonium, a radioactive waste by-product from spent reactor fuel, which can be extracted and reused as an energy source. The uranium fuel powering a reactor stays loaded in the reactor's core for four years after which time the energy-producing component of the fuel, an isotope called uranium-235, is mostly burnt up from its usual level of three per cent down to just one per cent. Only three per cent of the uranium in a reactor actually produces energy. When the uranium-235 is burnt up, the spent fuel must be removed from the reactor (called discharging) and the reactor reloaded once again with fresh uranium fuel. At this point each tonne of spent fuel waste contains 10 kilograms of plutonium. Roughly one per cent of the weight of the spent fuel is plutonium and the remainder is uranium mixed with fission products. There is however a surprising twist to the tale. The plutonium is not really waste. About 5 kilograms of the 10 kilograms of plutonium in each tonne of spent fuel is plutonium-239, which has similar energy-generation properties to uranium-235 present in ordinary uranium fuel. In fact uranium-235 can be substituted for plutonium-239 and this forms the technical basis for the production of MOX fuel used by some European and Japanese nuclear reactors today.

The commercial process used to make MOX fuel was jointly developed in the late 1950s by the Belgian Nuclear Research Centre SCK.CEN and Belgonucleaire. Belgonucleaire's Annual Report 2004 published in July 2005 showed that the company produced 39 tonnes of MOX fuel elements on a gross turnover of €59 million (£46 million at March 2008 currency exchange rates), signalling the commercial market price in European plants for fabrication of plutonium into MOX to be just over £1 million per tonne of heavy metal (£1,154 per kilogram) at 2004 prices.

This is a key pricing benchmark for two important reasons. Firstly, unlike uranium fuel element production that is priced in US dollars, the only commercial MOX plants operating worldwide are all based in Europe meaning that euros and pounds, not US dollars, drive MOX fuel pricing levels. Secondly, the collapse of the MOX market in 2006 signals that this European price was actually too high for nuclear utility customers to reasonably pay. The £1 million per tonne pricing level reflects the highest possible commercial price of MOX fuel that the market can bear. If the price of MOX fuel was competitive with low enriched uranium (LEU) fuel used in most commercial nuclear power stations today, then utilities would be expected to switch from LEU to MOX, particularly if this involved recycling the utility's own plutonium liabilities. To be economically viable the switching price would probably have to be somewhat lower than the LEU price, because of the extra investment needed to modify a reactor to accept MOX fuel elements and also the cost to relicense the reactor's nuclear safety case and gain regulatory approval. But in fact the long-term average market price of uranium fuel over the past decade has been much cheaper, at around £775 per kilogram (£650 per kilogram in 2001 and around £900 per kilogram in 2007). The £1,154 per kilogram market price of MOX fuel signalled by Belgonucleaire's collapse is nearly 50 per cent more expensive than LEU. For nuclear utility companies the choice is clear. LEU fuel is much more cost effective at around one third cheaper than MOX fuel and this is likely to remain the case for the foreseeable future.

Mined uranium ore prices are very volatile. For example over the past eight years uranium prices have varied from a low of $21 per kilogram in November 2000 to a high of $360 per kilogram in mid 2007, before falling to their recent level of about $163 per kilogram in March 2008. Although the spot price of uranium ore on the commodities market has a long history of being volatile, suffering from pricey supply shortages followed in turn by cheap over-supply, recent spikes in the spot price have not had much effect on long-term contract prices for manufactured uranium fuel. This is really for two main reasons. Firstly, negotiated prices for long-term uranium supply contracts are usually much cheaper at around one third of the cost of buying uranium on the commodities spot market. Buying on the spot market only makes sense to meet short-term supplies needed by nuclear utilities on a just-in-time basis. Secondly, because uranium ore only makes up about 25 per cent of the total cost of uranium fuel elements, any temporary spikes in ore prices have much less of an impact on the overall cost of fabricating uranium fuel. Uranium ore has to be processed, converted into gaseous form, enriched and then fabricated into fuel elements, and this makes up the majority (about 75 per cent) of total fuel costs. Like many commercial products, the cost structure is largely driven by the salaries of employing highly skilled nuclear labour, rather than procuring basic raw materials. The point is that LEU prices are not so much affected by fluctuations in the supply and demand of mined uranium ore, as they are by the gradual escalation of wages and salaries in response to national inflation trends.

Historically, the first peak in the production of uranium ore occurred towards the late 1950s from military demand. The second peak in the mid 1970s was the result of stockpiling following the 1973 OPEC oil crisis. By the early 1980s when Saudi Arabia had significantly increased oil production driving down global oil prices, uranium prices followed suit and dropped dramatically as the market crashed in response to a considerable oversupply of stockpiled uranium. The price of uranium ore continued to be badly affected by the dumping of military enriched uranium stocks onto the market during the 1990s. The 'Megatons to Megawatts' programme negotiated between the American and Russian governments in 1993 was part of an international nuclear arms limitation agreement, intended to convert highly enriched uranium (HEU) from dismantled Russian and American nuclear warheads into low enriched uranium fuel suitable for civilian nuclear power stations. These secondary supplies disrupted the commodities market because they caused uncertainty about how much uranium would actually be released through government channels rather than by primary commercial production from mines. The uncertainty is set to continue because in March 2008 the US Department of Energy (DoE) announced that it was considering releasing its own uranium stockpiles into the marketplace in quantities representing 10 per cent of total annual fuel requirements in the United States. The DoE's uranium sales strategy will need to cap the quantity of uranium the Department would sell annually to help protect American uranium producers. Secondary supplies from uranium inventories built up during the OPEC oil crisis and from weapons decommissioning still contribute 40 per cent of total supply but are beginning to run out. Primary production from uranium mines has been increasing to meet the decline in secondary supplies and also to meet the rising worldwide demand expected from new nuclear reactor build, particularly in the rapidly growing energy-hungry economies of China and Southeast Asia. The supply response is limited by the high cost of exploration and development of new mines, helping to drive up uranium ore prices.

Despite the recent volatility in the uranium market, it must be remembered that historically the long-term average price of uranium has remained low. The government's *White Paper on Nuclear Power* published in January 2008 analysed whether uranium supply disruptions could trigger sustained high prices that might rule out new nuclear power station build in Britain. This was an important question because the British Isles, like most of Western Europe, have no domestic high quality uranium deposits that could be mined economically. The major commercial uranium-producing nations are Canada, Australia, Kazakhstan, Niger and Namibia, who are all reassuringly pro-Western. The White Paper concluded that there were sufficiently diverse supplies of high-grade uranium ores available to meet future global demand, including the relatively small impact on world uranium demand from any new British nuclear programme. The government did not believe that uranium resources or the future price of uranium would be limiting factors for new nuclear power stations. But ominously for the future of the Sellafield MOX Plant (SMP), the White Paper concluded that any new nuclear power stations built in the UK should proceed on the basis that their spent fuel will not be reprocessed.

Taxpayer losses from SMP

The purpose of the Sellafield MOX Plant (SMP) is to manufacture plutonium-uranium mixed oxide (MOX) fuel for civil nuclear power reactors. SMP is co-located and integrated with the Thermal Oxide Reprocessing Plant (THORP) at Sellafield. SMP's current mission is to convert plutonium oxide, which has been separated from spent nuclear fuel in THORP, into MOX fuel for return to reprocessing customers. THORP and SMP are interdependent. THORP separates plutonium from spent nuclear fuel and SMP fabricates it into MOX fuel for re-use in nuclear power reactors. Together they provide a method of recycling plutonium back into a usable energy source for nuclear power utility companies to produce electricity.

SMP is constructed on four vertical levels with powder feed and homogenisation at the top level, followed by powder conditioning on the third level, pellet pressing and sintering on the second level, and fuel assembly at the bottom level. The plant is mainly designed to produce MOX fuel for PWR reactors using a short binderless route (SBR) process to blend uranium and plutonium oxide powders and prepare MOX granules for pressing. This is different to the simpler two-stage micronised masterblend (MIMAS) process invented by Belgonucleaire, which involves ball milling plutonium oxide powder followed by blending with uranium oxide. Although the design of SMP is capable of fabricating MOX from either THORP plutonium, Magnox plutonium or from military weapons plutonium, its regulatory justification licence granted in October 2001 by Margaret Beckett, the then Secretary of State Secretary of State for Environment, Food and Rural Affairs, restricted use of the plant to the manufacture of MOX "from plutonium which has been separated from foreign customers' fuel in THORP and which belongs to them" (*Justification for the Manufacture of MOX Fuel: Decision of the Secretary of State for Environment, Food and Rural Affairs and the Secretary of State for Health*, DEFRA, October 2001). SMP was therefore not licensed to manufacture MOX fuel from British plutonium or for British reactors. Its business case was based entirely on income from foreign exports of MOX derived from foreign spent fuel reprocessing at THORP.

BNFL's *Plutonium Working Group Final Report* published in March 2003, arguably the most comprehensive analysis of plutonium management ever published in the UK, confirms that when all of the NDA's existing spent fuel reprocessing contracts with foreign energy utility companies have been honoured, Britain will eventually store 37 tonnes of separated plutonium owned by foreign energy companies: 34.2 tonnes from reprocessing of foreign spent fuel in the THORP reprocessing plant and 2.8 tonnes from reprocessing of foreign spent fuel in the Magnox reprocessing plant, both of which are located at Sellafield. The latest figures available from the International Atomic Energy Agency (IAEA), published in September 2007, show that Britain already stores 26.5 tonnes (72 per cent) of the expected 37 tonne final inventory of foreign plutonium. Although nuclear energy utility companies could simply repatriate this plutonium back to their home countries, reprocessing customers generally prefer that the plutonium is converted into the much more user-friendly form of MOX fuel that can be reused in the utilities' own nuclear power stations. The SMP plant was intended to provide this service by carefully blending an average mixture of five per cent plutonium oxide with 95 per cent uranium oxide into MOX fuel elements. (Despite its name MOX actually contains mostly uranium with only a light sprinkling of fissile plutonium.)

The trouble is that despite the government's best intentions, SMP has turned out to be a very inefficient and expensive plant to run. If all of the 37 tonnes of foreign plutonium held in Britain is converted into 740 tonnes of MOX fuel using the SMP facility, the plant would need to operate for 285 years at its production capacity of 2.6 tonnes per year achieved in 2007. The running costs alone would be implausibly large, nearly £13 billion at 2007 plant manning levels and salary prices. Yet according to a favourable economic analysis carried out by the government's consultants Arthur D Little published in June 2001, *Assessment of BNFL's Business Case for the Sellafield MOX Plant*, SMP was originally designed to produce 120 tonnes of MOX annually over a design life of 10 years. After allowing six years for gradual ramp up of production to its full 120 tonne per year capacity, SMP should have been capable of fabricating all of the required 740 tonnes of MOX for foreign utility customers within a time span of just over six years. Today the market price would be around £854 million using the 2004 European pricing benchmark of £1,154 per kilogram charged by Belgonucleaire just before its closure in 2006. This would have been more than enough to offset BNFL's original £265 million build cost estimate in 1993 and even the actual £490 million capital cost spent by BNFL up to 2004. In fact the capital cost of SMP was effectively written off by the government when it was transferred from BNFL to NDA ownership under the Energy Act 2004. BNFL's losses were completely extinguished under Section 44 of the Energy Act freeing BNFL of any debt from its past investment in SMP. Today, with its £490 million sunk costs written off and future decommissioning liabilities of £92 million to be paid for by the NDA, the cost of operating SMP is largely driven by the salaries of its sizeable 811 person labour force running the facility on an intensive 24 hours a day, 7 days a week basis.

In September 2006 the NDA published an updated version of the *Review of the Sellafield MOX Plant and the MOX Fuel Business* prepared by consulting firm Arthur D Little in July 2006, the same firm that had advised the government on the economic justification for the startup of SMP back in 2001. Heavily censored with much financial data blacked out, the report nevertheless painted a worrying picture. Business confidence in the operational capability of SMP had deteriorated since startup in 2001 and SMP had failed to achieve its planned throughput and ramp up forecasts. The report stopped short of recommending closure of the plant but warned: "Looked at pessimistically, the improvement plans will fail to live up to expectations leading eventually to an irrevocable collapse in the business case and closure." The report went on to say: "SMP is a fragile plant with continuous availability problems, and unless availability improves then no amount of performance and yield improvement initiatives will make a significant difference. In other words, if the plant is continuously broken then you can not produce any meaningful output." Strong words from the world's oldest management consultancy firm.

Problems at SMP stem from its complex automated design. The plant is intended to operate on a mass-production continuous basis. But the highly automated design of SMP means that it is vulnerable to any equipment failures causing production bottlenecks, and the time taken to recover from these blockages. According to Arthur D Little, SMP suffered from a failure rate of 37,000 per year and production lines were either starved or blocked for 70 per cent of the available production time during working hours. When they were operating, the average yield of the MOX production lines was only 70 per cent meaning that 30 per cent of the MOX produced was scrapped, leading to waste storage problems. In European MOX plants the scrap rate usually ranges from eight to 15 per cent, and is often lower than 10 per cent. Under the ownership of the NDA, taxpayers now have a stronger interest in the commercial prospects of SMP and potentially have a say in deciding whether the plant should continue to operate. The economics of SMP, once mainly a private commercial matter for BNFL and its utility customers, now have a much stronger bearing on taxpayers who will have to fund any losses made by the NDA in running the plant. These losses take on an extra political dimension because the financial beneficiaries are foreign nuclear energy utility companies paying to have their plutonium converted into MOX. There is very little direct benefit to the British economy from converting foreign plutonium into MOX, other than supporting 811 full time jobs at SMP that are effectively being subsidised by British taxpayers. British reactors do not use MOX fuel for the simple reason that it is too expensive to buy, and too expensive to convert older British AGR reactors to load MOX. Only British Energy's Westinghouse-designed Sizewell B pressurised water reactor (PWR) nuclear power station that opened in 1995 has any realistic prospect of utilising MOX in the foreseeable future, assuming of course that the price of MOX falls substantially to become commercially competitive with LEU fuel. But as yet no commercial nuclear power station in Britain has ever been loaded with MOX fuel.

Short of divine intervention, it now seems almost certain that SMP will lose money for British taxpayers, the only question remaining being exactly how much. For SMP it is time to practise what business schools call realistic worst case (RWC) scenario planning. When drawing up corporate investment analyses, MBA students are taught to do them on an RWC basis. The question they must ask is: given what we know now, what is the worst future we can realistically foresee for this asset? SMP's approximate manufacturing cost curve, its break-even capacity and the potential scale of taxpayer losses are estimated graphically below. SMP is only economic if it can fabricate very large amounts of MOX resulting in low unit costs. The NDA runs a considerable financial risk if SMP does not achieve a sufficient MOX output capacity. This break-even point is estimated to be around 37.5 tonnes per year. The estimates are based on the author's own simplified calculations and assumptions derived from published information about SMP and particularly its employment cost structure.

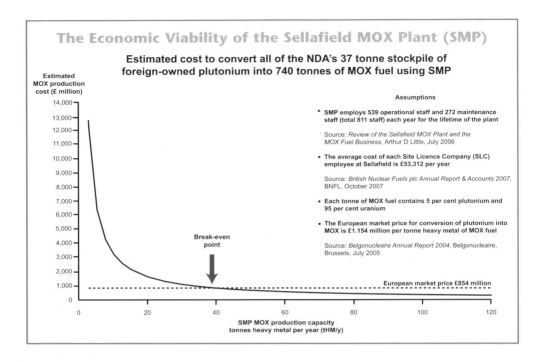

The Economic Viability of the Sellafield MOX Plant (SMP)

Estimated cost to convert all of the NDA's 37 tonne stockpile of foreign-owned plutonium into 740 tonnes of MOX fuel using SMP

Estimated MOX production cost (£ million)

Assumptions

* SMP employs 539 operational staff and 272 maintenance staff (total 811 staff) each year for the lifetime of the plant

  Source: *Review of the Sellafield MOX Plant and the MOX Fuel Business*, Arthur D Little, July 2006

* The average cost of each Site Licence Company (SLC) employee at Sellafield is £53,312 per year

  Source: *British Nuclear Fuels plc Annual Report & Accounts 2007*, BNFL, October 2007

* Each tonne of MOX fuel contains 5 per cent plutonium and 95 per cent uranium

* The European market price for conversion of plutonium into MOX is £1.154 million per tonne heavy metal of MOX fuel

  Source: *Belgonucleaire Annual Report 2004*, Belgonucleaire, Brussels, July 2005

Break-even point

European market price £854 million

SMP MOX production capacity
tonnes heavy metal per year (tHM/y)

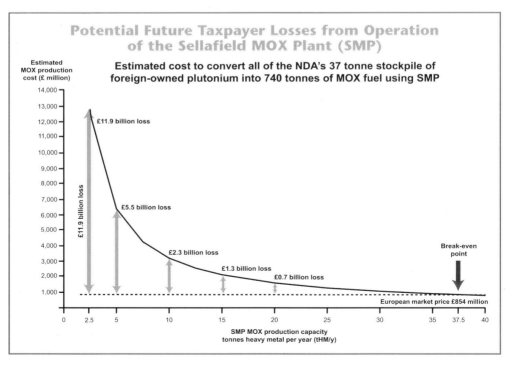

Potential Future Taxpayer Losses from Operation of the Sellafield MOX Plant (SMP)

Estimated MOX production cost (£ million)

Estimated cost to convert all of the NDA's 37 tonne stockpile of foreign-owned plutonium into 740 tonnes of MOX fuel using SMP

£11.9 billion loss

£11.9 billion loss

£5.5 billion loss

£2.3 billion loss

£1.3 billion loss

£0.7 billion loss

Break-even point

European market price £854 million

SMP MOX production capacity
tonnes heavy metal per year (tHM/y)

The graphs show the estimated total cost of converting the NDA's 37 tonne stockpile of foreign-owned plutonium into 740 tonnes of MOX for the export market, assuming an average plutonium content of five per cent by weight. The total cost incurred by the NDA can be estimated as a function of the production capacity of SMP in tonnes per year. The higher SMP's annual production capacity, the less time it takes to process foreign plutonium, reducing the manufacturing wages bill, resulting in lower total costs of production. For example if SMP improves its performance from the present 2.6 tonnes MOX per year, by successfully ramping production capacity up to 10 tonnes MOX per year, it will take 74 years to process 37 tonnes of plutonium into 740 tonnes of MOX. This means that the total cost incurred by the NDA will be £3.2 billion. However because the market sale price of 740 tonnes of MOX is only £0.9 billion, taxpayers will have to finance the £2.3 billion shortfall between the £3.2 billion manufacturing cost and the £0.9 billion sale price (all in 2007 prices). Increasing SMP's capacity to 20 tonnes MOX per year, would reduce the time to process the foreign plutonium to 37 years, and lower production costs to £1.6 billion, meaning that taxpayers would only have to finance the £0.7 billion shortfall between the £1.6 billion manufacturing cost and the £0.9 billion sale price (all in 2007 prices). SMP will break even when its production capacity rises to 37.5 tonnes MOX per year, reducing the time to process the foreign plutonium to 20 years. At that capacity the £854 million MOX production cost would exactly match the £854 million export sale price, much to the relief of the NDA, HM Treasury and taxpayers alike.

Of course nobody can quite be certain whether in the future SMP will or won't reach its 40 tonne production goal set by the NDA. As yet the taxpayer losses are only potential losses, ignoring SMP's £490 million sunk capital cost and £92 million decommissioning cost. They haven't actually happened yet and they depend on how well or how badly SMP performs over its remaining lifetime. But on 3rd March 2008 *The Guardian* reported that, in response to a Parliamentary Question, Energy Minister Malcolm Wicks had confirmed SMP produced only 5.2 tonnes of MOX during its six-year commissioning period from 2001 to 2007 (*Minister admits nuclear fuel plant produces almost nothing, The Guardian*, 3rd March 2008). The closure of SMP during Prime Minister Tony Blair's term of office, a plant that he had personally approved, was never really a serious option for government nuclear officials to consider. But the appointment of Gordon Brown as Prime Minister in June 2007 offers a rare second chance for a more realistic look at the economics of SMP, weighing the MOX needs of foreign utility companies against the significant financial risks to British taxpayers. SMP's economic future hangs in the balance.

Price elasticity in MOX markets

Plutonium is reputed to be high on the shopping list for would-be terrorists globally. Amongst the most toxic of substances in the world, in small amounts it is ideal as a radioactive pollutant spread by a terrorist dirty bomb or in larger amounts as a crude low-yield nuclear device, capable of destroying a few city blocks. According to William Langewiesche's book *The Atomic Bazaar*, there might be perhaps 20 serious buyers for a one-off atomic weapon worldwide. Miniaturisation is not important. You could hurt London well enough with a car-sized device locked into a shipping container or loaded into a private jet.

Plutonium in the form of mixed oxide (MOX) fuel has the dubious honour of being the first nuclear contraband known to have been trafficked on the black market. On 10th August 1994, Justiniano Torres, a 38-year-old Columbian national arriving on a Lufthansa flight from Russia at Germany's Munich Airport, was intercepted carrying 560 grams of plutonium and uranium mixed oxide. Half a kilogram of experimental MOX fuel had apparently disappeared from a Russian nuclear plant without ever being noticed or prevented. Not enough for a nuclear weapon but certainly enough for a dirty bomb. The purchaser, undercover officers from the German Foreign Intelligence Service BND, had apparently negotiated a sting deal worth $276 million for up to four kilograms of Russian MOX in 1994 prices. Today this would be worth $386 million (£192 million) making the black market price of MOX fuel to be worth an estimated £48 million per kilogram in 2008 prices. The commercial market price of MOX is rather lower at £1,154 per kilogram, although of course the buyers are blue chip energy utility companies buying supplies in bulk, rather than terrorists needing only a one-off marginal quantity.

In Britain plutonium exists in a peculiar state of being neither an asset nor a liability on the financial books of the Nuclear Decommissioning Authority (NDA) and nuclear utility companies owning plutonium stocks. Unlike stockpiles of other rare metal commodities such as gold or silver, plutonium has zero economic value; something that often comes as a surprise to investors unfamiliar with the nuclear sector. Nuclear utility companies don't declare their plutonium stocks as waste for fear it would add significant liabilities to their balance sheet, damaging shareholder value. But by the same token they can't declare their plutonium stocks as valuable energy resources either because the cost to convert plutonium into MOX fuel is higher than the price to buy ready-made uranium fuel. Plutonium remains stuck in zero value balance sheet limbo.

What these different price comparisons show from an economic perspective is that prices are elastic, meaning that different customer groups are willing to pay different amounts and that buying decisions are not always completely economically rational. This is especially the case for relatively hard to find goods or services such as MOX processing. The key to setting a price lies in understanding the logic motivating a particular customer's buying decision. Terrorists need to pay very high prices because would-be nuclear traffickers face stiff penalties if they are caught smuggling plutonium. Traffickers need high sales prices to make taking the risk of being imprisoned worth their while. The reason why nuclear power utilities might want to buy MOX fuel, even when it is nearly 50 per cent more expensive than low enriched uranium (LEU) fuel, is that MOX makes most commercial sense for utilities that are already contractually committed to having their spent fuel reprocessed. MOX fuel is the preferred choice for these foreign utility customers already owning plutonium under historic reprocessing agreements at the THORP plant.

In a political and strategic sense THORP is a multinational facility operating in a global marketplace. The major customers for its first ten-year baseload reprocessing contracts, for reprocessing of 7,000 tonnes of spent fuel, were Japan (38 per cent), the UK (31 per cent), Germany (14 per cent), Switzerland (6 per cent), Spain (2 per cent), Italy (2 per cent), Sweden (2 per cent) and the Netherlands (1 per cent) with another 4 per cent of spare capacity kept in reserve. Why would these customers want to pay for reprocessing of their own spent fuel when uranium fuel was so cheap to buy?

The answer lies partly in the political and economic fallout from the 1973 OPEC oil crisis. The economic rationale for THORP becomes clearer when seen in its historical context. THORP's spent fuel reprocessing contracts were negotiated in the 1970s, before the plant was actually built, at a time when the Western world was experiencing significant oil price volatility. In economic terms THORP was a hedge against Middle Eastern (and now Russian) energy dependency. Despite an eventual fall in oil prices, British political support for THORP continued into the 1980s under Conservative Prime Minister Margaret Thatcher's government. This was partly because THORP offered an energy hedge, this time against the threat of coal shortages from miners strikes organised by Arthur Scargill's left-wing National Union of Mineworkers. A previous miners strike in 1974 had triggered the collapse of Conservative Prime Minister Edward Heath's government and Mrs Thatcher was not about to let history repeat itself. Nuclear electricity generated from AGR and Magnox power stations helped to keep the lights on during this difficult period of industrial relations in Britain. THORP was clearly a political decision built with taxpayers money.

But the market forces motivating nuclear utility companies to actually use THORP today are different to the political drivers responsible for construction of the plant. Nuclear power utility companies which pay for reprocessing rather than dry storage of spent nuclear fuel often choose to have their separated plutonium converted to MOX fuel for reuse. Burning MOX fuel in a reactor is therefore a strategic choice rather than a fully commercial one. It does not matter that MOX is substantially more expensive than uranium fuel. However the recent trend towards deregulation and liberalisation of European electricity markets, losing their historic monopoly positions and forcing utilities to be more competitive, has driven energy utility companies to reduce costs where possible. Reprocessing of spent fuel is no longer an attractive commercial option because dry storage is substantially cheaper.

Before its financial restructuring in 2005 (which removed most of British Energy's spent fuel liabilities replacing them with a fixed-priced payment scheme to the NDA), British Energy estimated that its spent fuel costs would fall by a factor of six if it was allowed to pull out of THORP reprocessing contracts with the BNFL in favour of dry storage. But the contractual die was already cast in the 1980s and British Energy locked in to expensive reprocessing contracts with BNFL (now the NDA) for the long term, at least for reprocessing of its AGR spent fuel. The NDA has a choice whether or not to actually reprocess all of British Energy's AGR spent fuel in THORP. The European Commission pointed out in its State Aid decision in April 2006: "BNFL was under no obligation to actually reprocess the [AGR spent fuel] waste. It is only under a duty to manage it. According to the information available to the Commission, BNFL did not intend to reprocess all of it." British Energy did not sign any new THORP contracts in the 1990s for reprocessing of spent fuel from its newly-built Sizewell B PWR, ironically the only UK reactor today realistically capable of burning MOX fuel.

Captive players

The European Commission's Competition Directorate General (DG-COMP) is a powerful economic regulator that acts as a watchdog to help ensure fair play within the single market across the 27 member states of the European Union (EU). The EU comprises a single market created by a system of laws which apply in all member states that in theory guarantees the freedom of movement of people, goods, services and capital. The purpose of the single market is to ensure that national barriers to trade are removed and that trading systems are harmonised as far as possible. Harmonisation is fundamentally about creating level playing fields for competition across Europe. DG-COMP carries out market investigations and any companies that ignore its findings face stiff penalties. For example in February 2008 DG-COMP issued a record $1.35 billion fine against computer software maker Microsoft for failure to comply with an earlier 2004 competition ruling on openness within the software market.

In December 2004 following a complaint from Greenpeace, DG-COMP began a state aid investigation of Britain's Nuclear Decommissioning Authority (NDA) to determine whether the operation of SMP and THORP (plus some other commercial activities) was being unfairly subsidised by British taxpayers. Generally speaking the payment of state aid, where governments subsidise commercial companies using taxpayers' money, is unlawful because it breaches European Union competition law. Logically it would not be fair on other commercial MOX producers if the government subsidised the cost of running the NDA's SMP plant. DG-COMP published its market findings in its April 2006 report, *Commission Decision of 4 April 2006 on the State Aid which the United Kingdom is planning to implement for the establishment of the Nuclear Decommissioning Authority*. DG-COMP reached a fascinating conclusion about the market for spent fuel reprocessing and MOX fabrication services within Europe. In effect DG-COMP concluded that reprocessing is a political choice, not a commercial choice and that market economics do not really apply very well. This was a bombshell because in some ways MOX fuel is almost a commodity that is reasonably widely available to any nuclear utility that really wants to buy it. MOX is commoditized because supplies of MOX are more or less interchangeable, meaning that an energy utility company is not restricted to buying MOX from any specific manufacturer.

Belgonucleaire for example offered a merchant conversion service where it would take any utility company's plutonium and convert it into MOX for them. In fact BNFL had subcontracted MOX orders to Belgonucleaire in 2003 when SMP had failed to produce sufficient MOX fuel to meet its own customer orders. But instead DG-COMP concluded that MOX only makes sense if the intention is to reuse plutonium from existing reprocessing contracts. This constrains MOX production to the operators of existing reprocessing plants, meaning that effectively there is no free MOX market in the normal commercial sense. The MOX fuel you buy depends on the country where your fuel is reprocessed. In other words, MOX customers are locked in to a captive market situation.

This conclusion was, to say the least, unusual from a competition standpoint. When DG-COMP first opened its investigation in 2004 it announced: "The Commission doubts that the fact that SMP has only a few European competitors, of lesser capacity, can lead to the conclusion that there is no impact on trade. As a matter of fact, the mere existence of one competitor should be sufficient to conclude that there is an impact on trade." (*Official Journal of the European Union*, C315/10, 21.12.2004). This position is theoretically correct because, as we saw in Chapter 2 and Chapter 3, game theorists Jeremy Bulow and Paul Klemperer have showed the strategic importance of attracting just one extra player in any competitive process involving small pools of buyers and sellers. But evidently DG-COMP had changed its mind by 2006. What DG-COMP actually concluded was: "Under the prevailing economic conditions now and for the foreseeable future on the uranium market, reprocessing of waste fuel is a significantly more costly option than direct storage. The choice of reprocessing over direct storage is therefore very often a policy choice by government's of countries where nuclear waste plants are operated. Such a policy, which is often implemented by law or regulation, leaves very little if any room for competitive arbitrage by operators between the two options" (Paragraph 200). DG-COMP went on to say: "SMP's competition situation is also very specific. SMP fabricates MOX fuel. MOX can only be used in a limited number of nuclear power plants that have been designed or adapted for its use. SMP has only two commercial competitors at present: Areva and Belgonucleaire... Should SMP disappear, competition in the market would be restricted, at best to two companies with important common interests, and possibly even to a single company... Within this context the Commission considers that requiring early closure of SMP to mitigate competition concerns raised by the Measure would potentially create more competition concerns than it would solve" (Paragraphs 207-210).

As things turned out it was Belgonucleaire that disappeared, not SMP, in July 2006 just two months after publication of the European Commission's state aid decision. Today, Areva's MELOX plant in southern France, which opened in 1994, is effectively the world's only remaining commercial producer of MOX fuel, fabricating 145 tonnes annually using the highly efficient MIMAS technology originally developed by Belgonucleaire. According to the government's 2005 *Application for Approval of State Aid to the Nuclear Decommissioning Authority*, submitted by British Foreign Secretary Jack Straw to the European Commission, SMP had an operating capacity of "less than 100 tonnes per annum" and was forecast to hold a market share of around one quarter to one third of commercial MOX capacity globally. But with the failure of SMP to ramp up production, Areva's MELOX plant now massively dominates the commercial MOX market and could possibly use this leverage to increase prices if it wished. Foreign utility customers may potentially face a difficult choice in the future: either to repatriate their plutonium back to their own home countries, requiring expensive capital investment in robust plutonium stores, or to simply accept higher French prices for MOX fuel. On the face of it, an increase in the market price for MOX looks likely.

One nagging question remains about the demise of Belgonucleaire's Dessel MOX plant in 2006. If SMP and MELOX offered such a risky deal for foreign utility customers, then why did they not place even a small number of MOX fabrication contracts with Belgonucleaire instead? The economically rational choice for energy utilities would have been to hedge their mix of suppliers, transporting some of the utilities' plutonium banks from the Sellafield or La Hague reprocessing plants across to Dessel for conversion into MOX fuel. Placing just a few contracts with Belgonucleaire as a hedge would have been enough to exert significant downward pressure on MOX prices charged by the NDA and Areva. It would also have spread the commercial risk of supply interruption across three MOX plants rather than just one. Supply interruption is a major business risk for nuclear power stations loaded with MOX fuel because, once a reactor is converted to use MOX, it cannot easily be switched back to LEU fuel again. The MOX must be supplied and loaded into the reactor's core on a carefully scheduled timeline. Thirty seven PWR reactors in Western Europe currently operate with partial MOX core loading (typically 30 per cent of the reactor core is loaded with MOX fuel), 22 reactors in France, ten in Germany, three in Switzerland and two in Belgium. This precise timing requirement was the major reason why BNFL was forced to subcontract some MOX production to Belgonucleaire in 2003, in order to supply fuel urgently needed by a BNFL utility customer for a planned reactor refuelling outage.

The position today is that without SMP, commercial MOX customers are now reliant on just one plant, the MELOX facility, to supply all of their MOX fuel. If MELOX is shut down for any reason, for example caused by an accident or technical problem or regulatory intervention, the nuclear power station operators may face serious difficulty. Given these business risks the only conclusion that can be drawn is that the NDA and Areva must have been offering very good MOX pricing deals indeed to utilities, substantially below the market price that Belgonucleaire was offering as a merchant. French national interests may also have played a part: 59 per cent of the European reactors fuelled with MOX are in France. Since 2000 the MOX market has also suffered from a double whammy of the decision of the German government to gradually phase out nuclear power by 2020 along with the Japanese government's *de facto* moratorium on signing any new European MOX fuel supply contracts. British MOX fuel supply to Japan has effectively been suspended since 2000 after a MOX fuel data falsification incident occurred at Sellafield in 1999. The withdrawal signalled by Germany and Japan has severely depressed the commercial MOX market since these two countries are the largest MOX fuel users outside of France. The prospects for new nuclear build in Germany are weak but there is a chance that existing reactor units might get to operate longer than the 2020 nuclear phaseout agreement. Nevertheless Germany is not likely to remain a major export market for MOX and neither is Japan. Japan intends to produce its own MOX fuel domestically when the Japanese reprocessing plant at Rokkasho becomes fully operational. Time will tell whether the economic gamble apparently taken by utility companies betting on SMP and MELOX, rather than Belgonucleaire's Dessel plant, has actually paid off.

The emerging market in plutonium disposition

At European level many THORP reprocessing contracts were originally agreed during the 1970s in a different political policy climate than today, which was more favourable towards reprocessing as a strategic choice. Today low uranium prices have helped to make spent fuel reprocessing and MOX fuel manufacture commercially unattractive. Despite this downturn, MOX is re-emerging globally as a potentially competitive option for reactor-based plutonium disposition strategies, where the main objective is to destroy surplus plutonium in a nuclear power station, generating electricity as a useful commercial by-product.

The first such plutonium disposition plant is currently being built in America. In the 1990s the United States and Russia agreed to build one MOX plant each, expressly for the purpose of dispositioning 34 tonnes of military plutonium from retired nuclear warheads by converting it into MOX fuel for civil nuclear power stations. In 1999 the US Department of Energy signed a $130 million design contract with the DCS consortium comprising American nuclear energy utility Duke Power, the French MOX manufacturer Cogema (now renamed Areva NC) and the American nuclear services company Shaw Stone & Webster. The Savannah River Site (SRS) was selected as the site of the first American MOX disposition plant. Construction of the plant began in August 2007 and the facility is expected to be fully operational by 2016. Operated by Shaw-Areva MOX Services LLC, the Mixed Oxide Fuel Fabrication Facility (MFFF) will convert 34 tonnes of weapons plutonium into 680 tonnes of MOX over an expected 20-year plant lifetime. The nominal capacity of the American MOX plant is 70 tonnes MOX production annually.

To make sure that former weapons material could be successfully reused as MOX, an experimental trial was carried out beforehand known as the Eurofab Project. In 2003 Areva manufactured four MOX fuel assemblies at the MELOX plant in France using American military plutonium supplied under the Eurofab Project. In June 2005 the four MOX assemblies were successfully loaded into the Catawba nuclear power station in North Carolina, owned by Duke Power in the United States. It is intended that all of the MOX fuel produced from SRS will eventually be loaded at the Catawba nuclear power station. The US government will reimburse Duke Power for all MOX fuel-related operating and maintenance expenditures at Catawba, as well as any capital expenditures needed to modify the reactor for MOX fuel use.

The value of the commercial opportunity for the private sector to build MFFF has been reported as $4 billion. This commercial formula of paying utilities to use MOX for plutonium disposition now seems to be the most likely way forward for MOX production in the future.

The amount of plutonium produced in a nuclear reactor core depends on how long its uranium fuel has remained working inside the reactor, known as the fuel burn-up. A typical commercial 1GWe PWR nuclear power station produces about 710 kilograms of plutonium each year, of which 440 kilograms are burnt inside the reactor core itself and 270 kilograms remain behind in the spent fuel. Plutonium is generated as a waste by-product in the reactor but – and this is the crucial point – the reactor also destroys 60 to 70 per cent of the plutonium it creates depending on burn-up time. Despite their reputation for generating plutonium, nuclear reactor cores loaded with MOX fuel are in fact net consumers of plutonium. PWR reactors have plutonium conversion ratios of typically 0.6 to 0.7 with roughly the same ratio applying for both LEU and MOX fuel. In a MOX fuel element fresh plutonium production is insufficient to compensate for plutonium destruction. But usually only about 30 per cent of a typical PWR reactor core is loaded with MOX, the remaining 70 per cent being loaded with ordinary LEU uranium fuel. (Most commercial PWRs are restricted to MOX core loadings of between 30 to 50 per cent for technical safety reasons.) At 30 per cent MOX loading there is an exact balance between plutonium destruction in the MOX fuel and plutonium generation in the uranium fuel. MOX core fractions below 30 per cent are net producers of plutonium whereas MOX core fractions above 30 per cent are net destroyers of plutonium.

The ability of PWR reactors to burn MOX fuel has given birth to a new market opportunity, the deliberate destruction of unwanted governmental plutonium stockpiles. The idea is that nuclear utility companies would be paid by the government to use MOX fuel instead of buying LEU fuel on the open market. Because the cost of producing the MOX fuel would not be commercially competitive with the price of LEU fuel, the government would have to pay utilities a subsidy to use it. This rather unorthodox market concept is known as a non-commercial plutonium disposition strategy. Burning MOX as a waste management service (rather than as an energy resource) would reduce future balance sheet liabilities and is likely to be substantially cheaper than immobilising the plutonium and securely disposing of it in a geological repository. The idea of paying nuclear energy utilities to use MOX fuel upsets environmental groups because they see it as back door commercial subsidy for the nuclear industry.

Under European competition law (better known as anti-trust law in the United States), state aid subsidies are not allowed to be given by governments to help prop up industries.

Nevertheless, from an ethical standpoint, MOX as a plutonium disposition route has some clear practical advantages, not least that it actually destroys plutonium rather more simply than chemically immobilising it or burying it deep underground in a repository. The size of the government subsidy paid to the utility would be the difference between the £1,154 per kilogram market price of MOX and the £775 per kilogram market price of LEU, the subsidy needed being around £379 per kilogram of MOX. In practice the subsidy would probably need to be somewhat higher than this because PWR reactors must to be modified and relicensed to use MOX fuel, incurring extra costs for the nuclear utility company. The exact size of the subsidy is open to debate but one thing is sure: because nuclear utilities need a financial incentive to use MOX rather than cheaper LEU fuel, some form of subsidy arrangement is almost inevitable to make plutonium disposition commercially viable for utilities.

On the other hand it is possible that a new fleet of Areva EPR or Westinghouse AP1000 nuclear reactors likely to be constructed in Britain could be designed ready-made to use MOX fuel as part of a national UK plutonium disposition strategy. The 37 tonnes of foreign-owned plutonium that will be held in Britain is dwarfed by Britain's own eventual 109 tonne plutonium stockpile. BNFL's *Plutonium Working Group Final Report* published in March 2003 confirmed that when all of the Nuclear Decommissioning Authority's (NDA's) existing THORP and Magnox spent fuel reprocessing has been completed, the UK will own a stockpile of 109 tonnes of plutonium. The majority of the stockpile arises from reprocessing of Magnox fuel in the B205 reprocessing plant rather than in THORP. BNFL estimated in its *Plutonium Working Group Final Report* that 80 tonnes of Magnox plutonium will be produced (73 per cent of the UK inventory) of which 25 per cent (20 tonnes) would be directly suitable for MOX conversion and 40 per cent (32 tonnes) would be suitable with blending. A further 25 tonnes of plutonium (23 per cent of the UK inventory) will be generated from reprocessing of spent fuel in THORP from British Energy's AGR reactor fleet. The remaining four tonnes of the UK plutonium stockpile arises from past experimental reprocessing by the United Kingdom Atomic Energy Authority (UKAEA) at Dounreay.

The overall picture is that of Britain's 109 tonne plutonium stockpile, at least 77 tonnes (71 per cent) would be technically suitable for conversion to MOX fuel. This 77 tonnes is 'MOX-usable'. The latest figures available from the International Atomic Energy Agency (IAEA), published in September 2007, show that Britain already stores 79.5 tonnes (73 per cent) of the expected 109 tonne final inventory of British plutonium. As yet MOX has not been licensed by the nuclear safety regulators for use in any British reactors. Nevertheless the *Plutonium Working Group Final Report* provides a comprehensive overview of practical options for the potential use of MOX.

According to the working group, the best prospect for loading MOX fuel into a UK reactor is the British Energy Sizewell B 1.2GWe PWR, which could be modified and relicensed to accept a 30% MOX core loading of around 10.5 tonnes MOX per year, within a licensing timeframe of 3-5 years. Sizewell B is currently the UK's only commercial PWR station, although the government's 2008 *White Paper on Nuclear Power* indicated that construction of a new fleet of PWR nuclear power stations might begin as early as 2013 with them generating power by around 2018. Sizewell B has a planned operating lifetime to 2035 and probably will have a lifetime extension to at least 2040. Britain's 77 tonne stockpile of MOX-usable plutonium could be converted into an astonishing 1,540 tonnes of MOX fuel, assuming an average five per cent plutonium content. With a government subsidy of £379 per kilogram (above the LEU market price), this MOX stockpile might be worth around £584 million in economic benefit to nuclear utility companies. In theory the Sizewell B 1.2GWe PWR could operate for 147 years, with a 30 per cent MOX core loading, dispositioning 10.5 tonnes of MOX per year from the 1,540 tonne British MOX stockpile. A much more practical proposition would be to disposition the MOX stockpile using three new PWRs (almost certainly 1.1GWe AP1000s or 1.6GWe EPRs) over their reactor lifetimes of 60 years each. To make this vision a reality the government would need to have access to a reliable MOX plant that could convert Britain's 77 tonne stockpile of MOX-usable plutonium into 1,540 tonnes of MOX, spread over a timescale of not more than 60 years. In other words the government needs a MOX plant of at least 26 tonnes annual production capacity.

And therein lies the problem. At its current production capacity of 2.6 tonnes per year, the Sellafield MOX Plant (SMP) is clearly not up to the job. There are two obvious solutions, one expensive and one cheap. Either ship Britain's plutonium stocks to the 145 tonne per year French MELOX facility, returning the converted MOX fuel back to the UK for dispositioning in new British PWRs. Or build another MOX plant, 'SMP2', at Sellafield based on the more reliable Belgian MIMAS technology used at MELOX and Dessel. Surprisingly the expensive solution turns out to be conversion in France. At a market price of £1,154 per kilogram, the fabrication of 1,540 tonnes of MOX would cost the British government £1.8 billion (in 2007 prices). The capital cost to build SMP2 would likely be much cheaper than this. Arthur D Little's 2006 report, *Review of the Sellafield MOX Plant and the MOX Fuel Business*, neatly summarised the business case at the end of its Executive Summary: "Bearing in mind the current outlook on the potential throughput rate of SMP (only a few tonnes of plutonium per year at best)... such deliberations may seem premature. That said, if there were to be a realistic prospect of a domestic MOX programme at some point in the future, the SMP knowledge and skill base would be a valuable asset. Under these circumstances, greater weight could be attached to continuing to operate a MOX fuel business, potentially with SMP or a new MOX plant."

Investment in another British MOX plant now looks on the cards especially if this can be linked in some way to new nuclear reactor build. It may be feasible for a nuclear energy utility company to build a new PWR nuclear power station on NDA land if part of the deal with the NDA involved burning the British plutonium stockpile in the PWR. New nuclear build located on NDA land could potentially have a dual role both as a plutonium disposition reactor and also as a nuclear electricity generating station. Politically, the NDA has been careful to distance itself from the notion of actually constructing any new MOX fabrication plants or new PWR reactors, preferring any involvement to be as a landlord. Even so, it may be possible for the NDA to become more directly involved in the running of a plutonium disposition reactor. Section 10 of the Energy Act 2004 gives the NDA the power to operate electricity generating stations such as Magnox nuclear power stations and if necessary retired British Energy nuclear power stations. The Government made clear in its Explanatory Guidance to the Energy Act 2004 that this would not allow the NDA to construct new nuclear power stations. Section 3 of the Energy Act allows only the operation pending their decommissioning of nuclear plants. Despite this apparent restriction on new reactor build, Section 4 does allow the design, construction and operation of nuclear facilities for the treatment of matter or waste, which may include the treatment of separated plutonium as nuclear matter. In the Energy Act treatment includes the manufacture of nuclear fuel. This means that in principle both Section 4 and Section 10 operating together might legally allow the NDA to construct and operate a new MOX disposition plant and PWR nuclear reactor for the purpose of dispositioning surplus plutonium from the UK stockpile using MOX fuel. As noted above, such an NDA reactor could potentially have a dual role both as a MOX disposition reactor and also as a nuclear electricity generating station. MOX core loadings of up to 100 per cent are theoretically possible, although worldwide no commercial nuclear reactor has ever been licensed to operate at this level.

On 6th March 2008 the NDA announced a market engagement exercise with potential developers of new nuclear power stations, inviting them to submit proposals for commercial use of the NDA's assets. This engagement exercise will be the first real test of the private sector's appetite to become involved with new build partnerships with the NDA. The results could have important implications for the future of SMP.

Further Reading

Strategy Options for the UK's Separated Plutonium, The Royal Society, September 2007.

Review of the Sellafield MOX Plant and the MOX Fuel Business, Arthur D Little, Nuclear Decommissioning Authority, July 2006.

Uranium Resource Availability, AEA Technology, The Sustainable Development Commission, March 2006.

D Millington, Burning Plutonium in Sizewell B, AMEC-NNC, CoRWM Document Number 632, September 2004.

BNFL Plutonium Working Group Final Report, The Environment Council, March 2003.

Plutonium Management in the Medium Term: A Review by the OECD/NEA Working Party on the Physics of Plutonium Fuels and Innovative Fuel Cycles, OECD, 2003.

Assessment of BNFL's Business Case for the Sellafield MOX Plant, Arthur D Little, Department for Environment, Food and Rural Affairs, July 2001.

F Barker and M Sadnicki, The Disposition of Civil Plutonium in the UK, April 2001.

H Henderickx, Plutonium – Blessing or Curse?, European Interuniversity Press, 1999

Document Containing the Agency's Proposed Decision on the Justification for the Plutonium Commissioning And Full Operation of the Mixed Oxide Fuel Plant, British Nuclear Fuels plc Sellafield, Environment Agency, October 1998.

Chapter 5

Beyond Carbon: Nuclear Reactor Economics

The war on carbon

Science is based on practical observation, and observations tell us that the Earth is gradually getting warmer. Tomorrow's Britain could be much different from today's. The planet's atmosphere is slowly heating up, changing the world's climate. Carbon dioxide emissions from burning coal, oil and natural gas fossil fuels are the prime suspect. We are just beginning to see the early warning signs: melting glaciers, rising sea levels, flooding and hurricanes. In Britain and northern Europe we will probably experience this not so much as a global warming effect but more like a global wetting. In southern Europe and Africa the heating effect could be much worse, resulting in widespread famine and mass migration. Environmentalist and former US Vice President Al Gore's book, *An Inconvenient Truth: The Crisis of Global Warming* published in 2007, charts the rise in average global temperatures each year since 1860. From the 1980s onwards the rate of temperature increase has been accelerating. Of the 21 hottest years ever measured, 20 of them occurred in the last 25 years and 11 of the 12 hottest years so far have all taken place since 1995.

Man-made carbon dioxide emissions stay in the atmosphere for a long time, having an effective residence period of between 50 and 100 years. In total, about half of all man-made atmospheric carbon emissions released since the industrial revolution began in 19th Century Victorian England still remain there today, quietly absorbing the Sun's energy reflected as long wave radiation from the surface of the Earth – a process known as the greenhouse effect. Evidence from ice cores shows that carbon dioxide levels are higher today than they have ever been since the end of the last Ice Age about 10,000 years ago.

Those who doubt global warming tell us that what we are experiencing is just a temporary fluctuation in weather conditions, not a long-term pattern of fundamental climate change. But Professor James Lovelock, the British planetary scientist who developed the Gaia theory of the Earth as a self-regulating planetary system, paints a far more depressing picture of the future. His 2006 book, *The Revenge of Gaia*, warns of the likely human impacts of global warming: for people living in Britain and other northern European countries, much wetter weather, severe storms, flash flooding, sea level rises and inundation of Britain's vulnerable coastal cities including major economic centres such as London. And these are the lucky ones. For geographically less fortunate people living in Africa and Central America the implications of climate change verge on the Biblical: arid desertification of once lush tropical regions with widespread drought and famine, leading to mass migration of populations on an international scale.

Faced with these pressures, armed conflict is a possibility. The government's security strategy report, *The National Security Strategy of the United Kingdom – Security in an interdependent world*, presented to Parliament by Prime Minister Gordon Brown in March 2008, singled out security threats from climate change as a potential cause of future international disputes. The strategy report stated that climate change is potentially the greatest challenge to global stability and security, and therefore to national security. This is not by any means far-fetched. As the world's fifth largest economy, modern Britain is an ethnically diverse, tolerant and just society with a long history of acting to prevent humanitarian disasters world-wide. Yet relatively minor economic migration from Eastern Europe to Britain has already raised tensions between British people and foreign immigrants. Home Office statistics show that 766,000 Eastern European workers, just over half of which from Poland, legally migrated to Britain between 2004 and 2008. This pales into insignificance compared with a future surge of potentially millions of homeless foreign refugees displaced by the demographic impacts of African climate change driving them into European Union territory. This strategic threat raises genuine security concerns for Britain's national borders. A mass exodus of displaced North African people into Spain and on into southern Europe would be practically impossible to stop.

Probably the more immediate military flashpoint will not be over humanitarian migration but more familiar geopolitical conflicts about economic territory and energy security. The *National Security Strategy* warned that rising sea levels and disappearing ice will alter borders and open up new sea lanes, increasing the risk of territorial disputes – a thinly disguised reference to Russian claims of sovereignty over parts of the potentially oil-rich Arctic seabed lying beneath the melting ice caps of the North Pole. In 2007 the Russian Federation staked a claim with the United Nations to underwater territory extending from the Siberian coastline to the Lomonosov Ridge some 1,500 kilometres across the Arctic Ocean floor, symbolically planting a Russian flag on the seabed using a MIR mini-submarine. Anyone doubting the political seriousness of the situation, or the resolve of the Russian government, would do well to recall the oil-inspired Soviet invasion and occupation of Afghanistan between 1978 and 1989 – a situation that according to Professor Michael Klare's 2004 book *Blood and Oil* had helped catalyse the birth of al-Qaeda under its terrorist leader Osama Bin Laden who had fought the Soviets in Afghanistan.

The Iraqi invasion of Kuwait in 1990 was partly an attempt to corner the Persian Gulf oil market, temporarily giving President Saddam Hussein economic control of 20 per cent of proven world oil reserves, making him the world's second largest oil producer. In total 63 per cent of global oil reserves are located in the Arab petro-states of Saudi Arabia (25 per cent), Iraq (11 per cent), the United Arab Emirates (9 per cent), Kuwait (9 per cent) and Iran (9 per cent). Precise estimates of the size of proven oil reserves vary from year to year because as the price of oil goes down, the amount that is economically recoverable goes down. By the same token as oil prices rise, the size of world reserves that are economically recoverable also goes up. In mid April 2008, oil prices reached a historic high, passing $115 per barrel – meaning that economically recoverable world oil reserves are higher today than they have ever been at any point in the past. But this does not matter. Carbon's days as the world's leading energy resource are numbered. Sheik Yamani, Saudi Arabia's former Oil Minister and founding architect of OPEC, comments in Bjørn Lomborg's *The Skeptical Environmentalist*: "The Stone Age came to an end not for lack of stones, and the oil age will end, but not for the lack of oil."

The world's largest supply of energy isn't below our feet, it is above our heads: renewable energy derived from the sun. But this energy source cannot yet be harnessed economically on a large scale. Britain urgently needs a transitional stepping stone to help reach a fully decarbonised future, where cleaner renewable energy is generated without carbon emissions, without heating the planet's atmosphere and without generating harmful wastes. And that is where nuclear power can really help. Nuclear power is best viewed as a bridging technology to help buy time for renewable energy generation to fully develop and mature, while slowing down the worst effects of global warming.

The energy war fought in 1980s Afghanistan between Russia and the West was fought by proxy, with Western governments arming and funding local Mujahedeen resistance fighters. The 1991 Gulf War fought in Kuwait was different because it forced Britain and the United States into direct military conflict with Iraqi forces to secure and stabilise oil supplies to the West. The 2008 *National Security Strategy* tellingly highlighted energy security and the risks of British energy dependence on unfriendly regions, stating that competition for energy is one of the biggest potential drivers of the breakdown of the rules-based international system and the re-emergence of major inter-state conflict. It warned that China and Russia are already making control of energy supply a foreign policy objective.

The threat from climate change is as much military and economic as it is environmental. Global warming and security of energy supply are two sides of the same coin. Energy security is really the more important near-term issue for governments because, like the rest of Western Europe and the United States, Britain's economy can't function properly without foreign energy imports. But the political arguments for taking action on energy supply are sometimes presentationally dressed up in the language of global warming for ease of public consumption. Ask many green groups what is their opinion of the government's true energy priorities and they will tell you that behind the scenes, security of supply is the more important policy driver in Whitehall, not climate change nor the need to switch to low-carbon energy generation. For example, the Russian government has twice threatened to cut gas supplies to its former Communist ally the Ukrainian government, first in January 2006 and then again in March 2008. Ostensibly the dispute concerns Ukrainians enjoying cheap Russian gas supplies at below market price, as a hangover from their former communist past. But few observers doubt that the underlying cause is Russian political unease about an increasingly pro-Western Ukrainian government. In April 2008 Ukrainian President Viktor Yushchenko even applied to join the West's military defence alliance, NATO, with the support of US President George W Bush. The view from Moscow is that if Ukrainians want Russian gas then they can pay the same market price as their Western buddies. Western European governments have every reason to be concerned about energy dependence on a belligerent Russia.

Climate tipping point

The threat of climate change from man-made carbon emissions appears to be accelerating towards a global tipping point. Some official government institutions such as Britain's Environment Agency believe that some level of climate change is now probably inevitable. Malcolm Gladwell explains in his international bestseller, *The Tipping Point – How Little Things Can Make a Big Difference*, that in unstable systems liable to tip, change can happen not gradually but in one sudden moment. We may be quite literally living in the calm before the storm. The Earth's self-regulation system may already have crossed some invisible boundary line and we now await a massive self-correction by the planet's complex feedback loops – the self-correction being to eliminate the root cause of the carbon dioxide emissions responsible for destabilising the planet's atmosphere, namely mankind's industrial activities.

The strategic policy language of the Environment Agency has noticeably shifted from preventing climate change towards limiting, mitigating and adapting to climate change in an effort to head off some of the worst effects to come. The worrying possibility is that in the next 30 years we could pass the critical tipping point, triggering runaway global warming. In 2007 the American space agency NASA reported that the climate tipping point could be reached when the average carbon dioxide concentration in the Earth's atmosphere hits 450 parts per million. The pre-industrial level of 280 parts per million has increased to 383 parts per million today and is continuing to grow by 2 parts per million each year. This would make the year of the climate tipping point to be around 2040.

The question facing governments worldwide is how to fix the problem. The straightforward answer on which almost everybody agrees is to switch to low-carbon energy supplies. But politics gets in the way of implementation. There are three technically feasible solutions: renewable energy promoted by the green lobby; nuclear energy promoted by the nuclear lobby; and business-as-usual fossil fuel energy with a technological fix – carbon capture and storage – promoted by the oil, gas and coal lobbies. The dark green eco-warrior viewpoint is broadly that society should essentially de-industrialise itself, returning to cottage industry economies powered by wind, wave and solar renewable energy sources. And they are half right because this is essentially what has already happened in Britain. The rate of growth of Britain's carbon emissions has slowed by around 15 per cent since the 1990s but only because heavy industrial production has been outsourced to countries such as China.

Yet Britain's carbon footprint as measured by its economic consumption rather than by direct carbon emissions tells a different story. It has accelerated not braked. According to Dieter Helm, an Oxford University energy economist, if carbon outsourcing is factored back in then Britain's carbon emissions actually rose by 19 per cent rather than the government's official estimate of having falling by 15 per cent since 1990 (*Sins of Emission, The Wall Street Journal Europe*, 13th March 2008). Deindustrialisation and outsourcing of Britain's carbon pollution to manufacturing centres in China and the Far East merely displaces the problem, doing nothing to cut global carbon emissions.

Mainstream greens are more pragmatic, recognising that society will need time to adjust to a fully decarbonised energy system. For example, the environmental organisation Greenpeace favours the adoption of micro gas-fired combined heat and power (micro-CHP) as a transitional technology in which every new British home could become a self-reliant miniature power station generating its own hot water and electricity very efficiently. The microgeneration idea has already gained high-level political support from Britain's Conservative Party leader David Cameron who launched a Conservative Green Paper, *Power to the people – The decentralised energy revolution*, from Greenpeace's London HQ in December 2007.

The problem is that micro-CHP doesn't get around the basic problem of needing imported foreign gas supplies, and the inevitable energy security risks that they present. There is also the question of affordability. Microgeneration does not come cheap. Domestic systems cost around £10,000 to fully install, and the technology doesn't scale down very well. Micro-CHP is best suited to supplying blocks of flats, hotels, hospitals and office suites with near constant heating demands rather than small individual homes. Nevertheless micro-CHP is a good idea because it will help to cut electricity consumption, reducing overall demand on centralised energy transmission networks, hence lowering the amount of electricity that needs to be produced from larger carbon emitting fossil-fuelled power stations.

Nuclear electricity, a technology that produces virtually zero carbon emissions, surrounds us in modern Britain today. The night time baseload electricity used in Britain's homes and streets is mostly nuclear powered during periods of low energy demand in summer evenings. Yet within the next 15 years nearly all of the UK's ageing nuclear power stations will be permanently shut down. Britain will lose 18 per cent of her national electricity supply. The hope is that renewable energy, mainly wind and wave power, will rapidly grow to fill the energy gap left behind. But in 2007 renewables delivered just four per cent of total UK electricity generation. The question British politicians have had to deal with is: can renewables play catch-up and fill the energy gap just in time? Realistically, the answer is probably not. It generally takes around 40 years for new technologies to develop from open enthusiasm to widespread commercial application.

Unfortunately time is not on Britain's side: a climate change time bomb is set to go off around 2040. Without replacement nuclear capacity, the large-scale energy alternatives look strategically unattractive: either rely on Soviet *perestroika* and construct more gas turbine power stations fed from Russian and Kazakh gas fields; or build clean coal plants and hope that carbon capture technology can be quickly deployed and a place found to dump the climate-changing carbon emissions without risk of them escaping into the atmosphere.

Adjusting energy markets to deliver a low-carbon future

Limiting climate change without damaging the world economy depends on stronger and smarter market signals to regulate carbon dioxide. But markets do not like intervention by governments, which have a habit of upsetting the *status quo* and can introduce market distortions that may have unpredictable effects on trading. The freer people are to negotiate a deal amongst themselves, the more likely government intervention is to mess things up. For example, the introduction of the New Electricity Trading Arrangements (NETA) by the British government in March 2001 led to a wholesale power price fall in the energy market that virtually bankrupted the baseload nuclear generator British Energy by September 2002, triggering a financial rescue by the government. Similarly, in the 1990s, the dumping of highly enriched uranium (HEU) from military stockpiles onto the commodities market as part of a nuclear disarmament agreement between the American and Russian governments, led to a worldwide crash in uranium ore prices. The disposition of plutonium stockpiles currently being contemplated by governments internationally is arguably one of the factors that has damaged market confidence in the mixed oxide (MOX) nuclear fuel business, contributing towards a crash in MOX fuel prices in 2006.

Despite the unattractiveness of government intervention in the energy markets, the threat of climate change is so serious that 'business as usual' (BAU) is not a realistic option. The market framework has to change.

But before designing adjustments to energy markets it helps to think about what a low-carbon future might look like. The surprising answer is that it would look much the same as today. By the year 2040 – the climate tipping point – most people will probably be busy doing the same things as they do now, raising families and working, but the enabling technologies they use to do these things will be different and much better. For example, in the 1950s, coin-operated Wurlitzer jukeboxes made pop-music accessible to young people.

Wurlitzers were about the same size and weight of a book cabinet and had a playing capacity of 100 songs recorded on 45 rpm vinyl discs. Today young people still love listening to pop music, just as their parents and grandparents did 50 years ago, but the enabling technology has changed tremendously. Apple's ubiquitous *iPod* music player, the fashion accessory of school children everywhere, has a capacity of thousands of songs with trivial energy consumption, yet can be held in the palm of your hand. The basic human activity of listening to pop music has not changed, just the technology used to do it.

Similar technological leaps have occurred in many other areas. Take maths homework for example. In 1940s school children used slide rules. By the 1980s they used electronic calculators. Yet basic computing technology already existed in the 1940s, developed in secret by the British at Bletchley Park to crack the German wartime Enigma code. It took another 40 years for computers to become commercialised and widely available to the general public, initially as calculators in the 1970s then later as personal computers in the 1980s. We are seeing much the same trend in the evolution of television technology. Regular BBC Television broadcasts began in the 1940s. By the mid 1960s viewers were watching three TV channels in black and white. Today in 2008 many people are watching over 100 channels by digital satellite, an enabling technology invented some 20 years after the BBC began regular TV broadcasting.

The point of these comparisons is that the advanced energy technologies that will be widely used around 2040 almost certainly already exist in prototype form today. But they are presently either too expensive or need further development to make them work better. Just as cars displaced horses, jukeboxes displaced live music, television displaced theatre and calculators displaced slide-rules, fossil fuels will be eventually be displaced by low-carbon generating technologies because there is a fundamental market need for them. Sheik Yamani's prediction that the oil age will end but not for the lack of oil, is almost certainly true.

For the foreseeable future at least, cutting carbon emissions and creating energy security in the Western world really means going nuclear. The problem is that present-day energy markets are designed to deliver the least-cost solution, not the greatest-benefit solution.

In 1982, Prime Minister Margaret Thatcher's Conservative Government fundamentally changed the way energy is supplied in the UK. Instead of government taking responsibility for supplying electricity and gas, Energy Minister Nigel Lawson began privatising energy supply in Britain. During the two decades since privatisation gas power has generally been cheaper than coal power, nuclear power or wind and wave power. The result has been a 'dash for gas' during the 1990s. By 2020, about 55 per cent of energy generated in the UK will probably be from gas generation. Gas-fired power plants are the most economic choice because they are cheaper to build and they can operate flexibly, increasing their output to meet increases in electricity demand then reducing their output again when electricity demand lowers. Nuclear power plants are about four times more expensive to build than gas-fired plants. They are inflexible and cannot easily be powered up or shut down to meet changes in electricity demand, but they do generate large amounts of baseload electricity very reliably. Renewable plants are expensive and unreliable. They produce electricity intermittently depending on local wind and tidal conditions. They are inflexible and cannot meet changes in energy demand. At best only about 25 per cent of renewable generation can be safely added to the national electricity grid before the grid becomes too unstable. Grid operation with increasing quantities of wind or wave power is a major problem risking the collapse of centralised electricity grids, knocking out power over a wide area. Such a power blackout happened in North America in August 2003 affecting 50 million people, apparently triggered by trees touching power cables. Although not caused by power fluctuations from renewable energy generation, the incident nevertheless highlights the tricky dynamics of exactly balancing energy supply with energy demand across national electricity grids.

Britain's ageing coal power stations that once generated almost 70 per cent of electricity in the early 1990s have now declined to around 37 per cent of UK generation and are expected to carry on reducing to about 25 per cent by 2020. New European environmental measures are expected to further hasten the closure of old coal plants. Despite gas's economic dominance, gas has a serious downside: when natural gas is burnt it produces carbon dioxide, which is thought to be the main cause of global warming. Meanwhile nuclear and renewable energy produce almost no carbon dioxide.

This raises a fundamental question about Mrs Thatcher's energy markets. Markets always deliver the most competitive outcome where the best price wins. But they can't always deliver what is in the best national interests of a country. Only governments can do that. If left on their own, Britain's energy markets won't shift towards low-carbon supplies. They are simply too expensive compared with the cheaper alternative of gas-fired generation. As with all market-based systems, the solution lies in finding ways to incentivise commercial energy producers to generate low-carbon electricity supplies demanded by governments. Carbon trading might be the answer.

Carbon trading

The importance of creating a market-based system for limiting carbon pollution from energy producers was first signalled in the British government's July 2006 report, *The Energy Challenge – Energy Review Report 2006*. Previous energy white papers had dealt with the government's usual priorities of economic growth, rising energy demand and lower prices for consumers. But this review was different. The first chapter focussed squarely on the issue of the decade – valuing carbon. The government rightly argued that the only way businesses could realistically be expected to reduce their carbon emissions was if an international system of carbon trading was created, operating worldwide on a level playing field. The reason that carbon dioxide emissions have risen to near dangerous levels is because the Earth's atmosphere is used and abused for free by industry. The government realised that to prevent climate change, society needs to put an economic price on carbon pollution. In effect what the government had proposed was to partially privatise the atmosphere.

Governments generally have four main options for reducing carbon dioxide emissions produced by business activities: they can ban carbon emissions completely; they can limit them through tighter emissions regulation; they can heavily tax the emissions; or they can charge polluters for the right to carry on making emissions. Different policy solutions work better in some situations more than others. In the transport sector for example, where sources of carbon pollution are spread amongst a European fleet of 224 million vehicles (87 per cent of them cars), the European Commission (EC) plans to set strict limits on carbon emissions from new cars produced by vehicle manufacturers. The British government already taxes vehicle owners annually according to a sliding scale based on their carbon emissions.

The energy sector is different because major sources of carbon dioxide emissions from power stations and heavy industry are concentrated amongst a much smaller group of just 11,000 businesses spread across Europe. The best solution for cutting carbon emissions from these businesses turns out to be a market-based carbon trading system, which charges polluters for the right to carry on polluting. In 2005 the European Union (EU) designed a continent-wide carbon trading market called the Emission Trading Scheme (ETS), a mandatory 'cap and trade' system for European businesses. The idea of a cap and trade market is that national governments set a fixed cap on the maximum amount of carbon dioxide that can be emitted each year, and polluters trade their emissions allowances with each other. Businesses that can easily reduce their carbon emissions through low cost pollution control investments, can sell on their excess emissions allowances to other European businesses who cannot cut their own carbon emissions without paying for major decarbonising investments. This means that the most cost-effective solutions can be taken up first by businesses who are the best placed to adopt them. At the same time, the annual emissions ceiling is gradually reduced centrally by the EC so that total carbon emissions across all EU states continue to fall.

In theory the carbon market should be a highly efficient and low cost way of reducing carbon emissions because it gives a financial incentive to lazy polluters who can easily cut their emissions, while at the same time allowing carbon-intensive businesses to carry on trading albeit with higher operating costs from purchasing emissions permits. If emissions cuts prove costly demand for permits will rise, driving up their selling price. On the other hand, prices will fall if low cost 'end of pipe' technologies for abating pollution appear or if slow economic growth weakens the major industries that produce carbon emissions.

The genius of the European carbon market is that it created valuable property rights quite literally out of thin air, avoiding the usual blunt policy instruments of taxation and regulation that are normally imposed by governments to cut unwanted emissions. Moreover, the degree of emissions cuts achieved will depend on the price of carbon, so that the market itself will drive emissions reductions. Around 80 per cent of the total volume of carbon trading deals between companies are arranged on the European Climate Exchange (ECX), which operates much like a stock market, trading carbon permits instead of shares.

One of the stranger consequences of belonging to an international carbon trading scheme is that emissions may not necessarily drop in Britain. If investment in reducing carbon emissions remains expensive relative to more modern EU plants, then it will be cheaper for British companies to buy carbon permits from other European businesses. In economics language, the marginal abatement costs (MACs) of reducing pollutants vary between different countries. The total carbon emissions output will be cut across Europe as a whole but the downside is that buying foreign permits could potentially push up costs for British businesses, making them less competitive than similar European firms. On the other hand, carbon emissions may fall anyway as Britain increasingly shifts away from heavy industry towards a de-industrialised knowledge-based economy. Carbon trading may ultimately hasten the decline of Britain's manufacturing base, leaving energy production as the remaining major industrial source of carbon pollution.

The market's actual experience of carbon trading has been patchy since the European ETS began its first trial period that ran from 2005 to 2007. The EC's *Directive 2003/87/EC* ruled that most allowances should be allocated to installations free of charge, at least 95 per cent during ETS Phase I and at least 90 per cent during ETS Phase II. Emissions permits were allocated to companies according to their historic emissions levels – a process known as 'grandfathering'. Unfortunately, governments grandfathered these permits rather too generously to firms based in their own home countries, resulting in a carbon price crash in April 2006. When carbon markets are created it is important that the quantity of emissions permits must match the real output of carbon emissions from firms, which can be difficult to verify. If too many permits are allocated, a fall in the value of each permit eventually results, which is what happened in 2006 when the over-allocation was discovered by European carbon traders and prices crashed from about €30 per tonne to €10 per tonne.

The EC is gradually tightening the rules on carbon trading for Phase II of the ETS running from 2008 to 2012. The Commission's 'soft landing' market reforms include centralised scrutiny by the EC of permit allocations granted by individual governments, with an intention to eventually auction 100 per cent of permits to the energy sector under ETS Phase III by 2013 rather than allocating them to energy companies freely. European carbon permits are currently trading at around €22 per tonne (£17 per tonne) under ETS Phase II as of April 2008.

Nuclear power and carbon trading

Carbon trading is extremely important for the future economic viability of nuclear power, despite the fact that nuclear energy is excluded from the European Emission Trading Scheme (ETS) – for the simple reason that nuclear power stations do not emit carbon dioxide. There would be no point in selling carbon emission allowances from a nuclear power station because they do not emit any carbon. By the same token nuclear power stations would not need to buy carbon emissions permits either. The reason why carbon trading is so important for the economics of nuclear power stations is that carbon trading pushes up generating costs for its two main rivals, gas-fired and coal-fired power stations. The higher the price of carbon permits then the higher the costs that have to be borne by fossil-fuelled generators, pushing up wholesale electricity prices. Nuclear power benefits from carbon trading because carbon trading makes energy more expensive for everybody else. For fossil fuel generators the price of an emissions allowance causes a proportional rise in the price of electricity, as electricity generators include the price of an allowance as part of their costs. This price increase means an increase in income for nuclear power, and other forms of zero carbon generation such as wind and wave power, without any corresponding increase in cost because they are not required to have or to buy any emissions allowance permits.

A key signal of just how important carbon trading is for nuclear power was buried away in a technical annex of the July 2006 report, *The Energy Challenge – Energy Review Report 2006*. The annex graphically compared the cost ranges of different forms of electricity generation under various carbon price scenarios. With no carbon price included (in other words where the carbon price is €0 per tonne) the two cheapest forms of electricity production are the latest generation of pulverised fuel advanced supercritical (PF-ASC) coal-fired plants fitted with flue gas desulphurisation (FGD), and also combined-cycle gas turbine (CCGT) gas-fired plants, with nuclear in third place. If the carbon price rises to €25 per tonne (similar to trading prices today) then nuclear power becomes the cheapest form of electricity generation, followed closely by PF-ASC/FGD coal-fired plants then CCGT gas-fired plants. If the carbon price rises even higher to €36 per tonne, similar to its early peaks under Phase I of the ETS, then nuclear becomes even more cost-competitive compared with coal and gas. Overall, the economics of nuclear power critically depend on assumptions made about future carbon and gas prices, set against nuclear generation costs.

But not everybody agrees with the advantages of carbon trading. The importance of carbon trading for nuclear power is not lost on green groups such as the Amsterdam-based World Information Service on Energy (WISE), which has complained that "the carbon market artificially created by the ETS is a brilliantly concealed way to make taxpayers foot the bill for the revival of the nuclear industry" (*Nuclear Monitor*, No. 665, 28th January 2008). WISE makes a reasonable point although the criticism is slightly unfair because carbon pricing simply forces fossil fuel generators to pay for their carbon pollution, whereas they had previously avoided these costs in the past. In economic terms, carbon pollution is an externality which the ETS successfully forces energy businesses to internalise by factoring pollution costs back into the total market price of electricity generation.

There is however a major catch. Although carbon trading is regarded by many as the economic saviour of the nuclear industry, it has a serious downside for nuclear utility investors: what if the costs of decarbonising the world economy turn out to be cheap? The result would be an overall fall in the price of carbon permits, arising from excess of permit supply because fewer businesses would need them, damaging the economic case for investment in nuclear power. Nuclear power would not be needed if carbon emissions could be prevented cheaply. This is a real risk for nuclear investors because a similar market event actually happened in the 1990s with the world's first emissions trading market, developed by the Environmental Protection Agency (EPA) to control sulphur dioxide emissions from power stations in the United States. High levels of atmospheric sulphur emissions were a problem in the US because they caused acid rain, damaging plants and trees and acidifying lakes, killing their aquatic ecosystems. After negotiations with power producers to retrofit emissions scrubbers had stalled, the EPA decided to set up a permit-based auction for the right to emit sulphur dioxide. In fact the design of the European carbon emissions trading scheme was partially modelled on the EPA sulphur emissions trading system. Power producers argued that the cost of fitting FGD would be prohibitively expensive, leading to market expectations of high permit prices. Even the EPA estimated that the cost of reducing sulphur emissions by one tonne would probably be in the range from $250 to $700 and might be as high as $1,500 per tonne. But when the EPA conducted the auction in 1993 very few polluters made high bids. Pollution abatement proved cheap to install and by 1996 sulphur permit prices had fallen to $70 per tonne. Getting rid of sulphur dioxide emissions was so cheap that few American businesses were willing to pay much for the right to keep producing it.

This American experience offers an important warning signal for nuclear investors gambling on sustained high carbon prices to make nuclear power economic. If a cost-effective transformational technology emerges in the future for limiting carbon pollution, then the economic case for nuclear investment will be seriously undermined because any resulting depression in the carbon price will automatically lead to a fall in electricity prices. Remember that the *Energy Review Report 2006* clearly showed that the latest designs of coal-fired and gas-fired generation are cheaper than nuclear generation as the carbon price drops towards €0 per tonne. What's more, the capital investment in new nuclear plants will already have been paid for up front by investors, effectively locking them in for decades. Investors stand to lose serious money if the wholesale power price falls below the cost of nuclear generation as it did in Britain in 2002. The bottom line is that if a magic bullet carbon abatement technology is developed sometime in the future, crashing the carbon trading price, then new nuclear plants would most likely become unsaleable stranded assets needing a government takeover again.

It was really for these unstated reasons that the government's May 2007 *Meeting the Energy Challenge – A White Paper on Energy* and the subsequent January 2008 Energy Bill both promised greater certainty for investors through action to underpin the price of carbon if the EU ETS failed to deliver a sufficiently high carbon price by Phase III in 2013 – the critical date when energy utility investors would need to commit their capital financing for building a new generation of nuclear reactors in Britain. With their five-year construction period, new reactors would need to start coming online from 2018 onwards to replace nuclear capacity lost from closure of Britain's AGR nuclear power station fleet by 2023. The option of state intervention to maintain the price of carbon is highly controversial. After all, if the carbon market functions properly there would be no need to artificially prop up the trading price. The carbon price itself signals whether nuclear is really needed. A high price would signal that nuclear is necessary, while a low price would signal that it is not. At a carbon price of €22 per tonne (£17 per tonne) – the price as of early April 2008 – new nuclear stations ought to be the cheapest form of electricity generation, slightly better than gas and coal.

At present, the advanced technology most likely to disrupt the carbon market is carbon capture and storage (CCS). Clayton Christenson explains in his 1997 book, *The Innovator's Dilemma: When New Technologies Cause Great Firms to Fail*, that disruptive technologies can radically change established market structures very quickly. CCS is a disruptive technology under development by the oil and gas industries, and clean coal industries, who have the most to gain from making CCS work and the most to lose if it does not. The basic idea is that carbon emissions from heavy industry can be trapped and stored underground, most likely by dumping them in the same spent oil fields where the carbon originated. CCS applied to a modern conventional fossil fuel power plant could reduce carbon dioxide emissions to the atmosphere by approximately 90 per cent compared to a plant without CCS. But capturing and compressing carbon dioxide consumes energy increasing the fuel needs of a plant with CCS fitted. As a result CCS would increase the cost of energy produced from a new power plant fitted with CCS, and would also incur disposal charges for dumping the emissions in a suitable geological storage location.

Innovation efforts are not just limited to end of pipe carbon trapping solutions. Sir Richard Branson's Virgin Group launched its *Earth Challenge* competition in February 2007, offering a $25 million prize for anyone who can come up with a system for removing greenhouse gases directly from the atmosphere.

In practice, less spectacular but gradual improvements in better energy efficiency of the Wurlitzer-to-*iPod* variety are likely to threaten long-term price stability in the carbon trading market. For example, in September 2007, New Labour's Environment Secretary of State Hilary Benn announced joint plans with British retailers to phase out high energy tungsten light bulbs by 2011. Greenpeace has estimated that if every light bulb in a UK home was replaced with an energy efficient bulb, Britain could save 3.5 per cent of its total electricity demand, roughly equivalent to the output of two modern Sizewell B nuclear power stations (*Energy Security in a Cold Winter*, Greenpeace Brief, November 2005).

There is one remaining potential market trap for unwary nuclear energy investors: climate scientists might have got their sums wrong. Global warming has become the great environmental worry of our day. Yet in the 1960s and 1970s the environmental movement was more concerned that future generations of society would suffer a 'nuclear winter', similar to that thought to have killed the dinosaurs, where the prehistoric atmosphere cooled rather than warmed. Despite the present physical evidence for global warming it is possible that the scientific community might in future decide that man-made carbon dioxide emissions are not responsible for climate change. Or that the rate of global temperate increase turns out to be much slower than forecasted by present-day computer models. Climate sceptics point out that predictions of global temperature rises strongly depend on assumptions made about the sensitivity of the Earth's positive feedback loops to carbon dioxide. The feedback loops act as gears, amplifying the climatic effect of carbon dioxide resident in the atmosphere. The gearing factor is around 60 to 80 per cent. Because the most recently observed temperature rises have actually been lower than computer predictions – 2008 is expected to be cooler than previous years for example – the gearing multiplier effect from atmospheric carbon dioxide might turn out to be less than expected. The US website *www.climate-skeptic.com* suggests that carbon dioxide pollution is more nuisance than catastrophe. If the Earth does prove to be resilient to carbon dioxide levels, or if global warming continues but is found not to be caused by industrial carbon emissions, then the price of carbon permits would fall as investment in carbon pollution prevention would no longer be needed. There is clearly a risk to nuclear energy investors that new scientific knowledge about the origins and causes of global warming might result in a revaluation by the markets of the carbon trading price, rendering nuclear power stations uneconomic. It is precisely for this reason that some nuclear lobbyists remain privately cautious about promoting nuclear energy based solely on its low-carbon environmental credentials. Backing the climate change horse might backfire on nuclear investors unless the government guarantees a minimum price for carbon.

Conclusions on new nuclear investment

The crucial difference between building a modern nuclear power plant today compared with the past is that the private sector, not the government, will be constructing and paying for them. The financial motivation for shareholders investing their money in blue chip companies is to see the value of their investment grow faster than if the money had been deposited in a bank account earning interest. Investors expect steady growth in earnings and share price. Benjamin Hunt, a *Financial Times* journalist, explains in his 2003 book, *The Timid Corporation – Why Business is Terrified of Taking Risk*, that managing for shareholder value has become the preoccupation of Chief Executive Officers (CEOs) worldwide. CEOs are lauded when their company share prices rise and sometimes fired when they fall, usually after profit warnings. The corporate bonus payments of senior executives are geared to reflect this shareholder imperative, rewarding sustained growth and higher company profits.

Not surprisingly, the investment strategies of Chief Executives running big companies tend to be dominated by short-term thinking rather than long-term investment planning. Unlike family run businesses it is hard for most Chief Executives to worry too much about the long-term future of a publicly owned company, when most likely they will no longer be employed there after five or ten years at best. Short-termism is the order of the day.

Even when the shares of publicly-listed companies are bought out by private equity firms returning them back to private ownership, the pressure for fast profits usually increases. Private equity firms make their money by buying underperforming companies, nurturing them and cutting costs to improve their business profitability, then selling them on again within around five years at profit margins of 20 per cent or more.

Given these pressures, at first sight it is difficult to see why energy utility investors might want to put their hard earned money into new nuclear power plants. They have some serious economic downsides for nervous private sector investors and the Chief Executives of utility companies. Nuclear plants are capital-intensive long-lived assets costing around £2 billion each (after factoring in pricing discounts for multiple reactor orders) with a 40- to 60-year generating lifetime. The capital cost of an 'nth-of-a-kind' (NOAK) reactor should be 10 to 20 per cent cheaper than a 'first-of-a-kind' (FOAK) reactor because of the lessons learned in the construction and deployment of earlier units. The manufacturing learning curve generally flattens out after 5 to 7 repeat units have been built, although this experience could be gained very quickly if a standardised reactor design such as the EPR or AP1000 were deployed worldwide. Even so, nuclear reactors are expensive to build, making them vulnerable to fluctuations in national interest rates.

The cost structure of a typical nuclear power station is nearly the opposite of that of a gas-fired power station. Nuclear stations are expensive to build but they have cheap fuel running costs, whereas gas-fired power stations are cheaper to build at £500 million, but have expensive fuel running costs. The government's July 2006 Energy Review report, *The Energy Challenge*, noted that the price of uranium nuclear fuel represents only about 11 per cent of the lifecycle cost of a nuclear power station, whereas the price of gas fuel makes up 71 per cent of the lifecycle cost of a gas-fired power station. For investors funding capital investment, building a nuclear power station is basically a gamble on future capital interest rates, whereas building a gas-fired power station is largely a gamble on gas price volatility. If gas prices rise too much, costing the energy utility more money to generate electricity than the price for which the electricity can be sold, then the gas-fired power stations can be temporarily mothballed by the utility, avoiding the high cost of fuel and limiting the financial exposure of the utility to interest rate payments on the low capital cost of the plant. When gas prices drop back down again or wholesale power prices rise, the mothballed gas-fired generating plant can be speedily recommissioned back into operation. In contrast, investors in nuclear plants are much more vulnerable to fluctuations in national interest rates over the 60-year generating lifetime of the plant. Because the capital cost of a nuclear station is four times higher than a gas-fired station, which all has to be paid for up front by the nuclear utility, any changes in interest rates or falls in wholesale power prices can have a major effect on the profitability of the nuclear station.

The truth is that nobody can predict interest rates over a 60-year timeline. At best, national economic trends in Britain seem to follow cycles measured in decades; the mid 1970s through to the mid 1980s were inflationary, the mid 1980s through to the mid 1990s were recessionary, while the mid 1990s through to the mid 2000s have seen a welcome period of relatively stable economic growth with correspondingly low interest rates. There are some warning signs that this cycle may be about to change again and that we are entering a new period of economic uncertainty. America's fifth largest bank Bear Stearns had to be rescued by the US government in March 2008 as did Britain's Northern Rock bank, which was nationalised by the British government in February 2008, safeguarding £55 billion of Northern Rock's mortgage lending liabilities.

Moreover, the falls in wholesale electricity prices experienced in Britain and America during the first half of the 2000s resulted in some commercial nuclear power stations temporarily becoming stranded assets – loss-making assets that nobody was willing to buy at a fair market price. The utilities were stuck with shouldering losses from nuclear stations and the debt from the capital cost of the power plants having to be restructured by governments and lenders, until wholesale power prices rose back up again as they eventually did.

Against this difficult investment background, why would any rational private sector investor possibly want to invest their money in nuclear power? The answer is that despite its wobbly economics, nuclear provides security of supply with zero carbon emissions, while also providing a hedge for energy companies against exposure to the price volatility of foreign gas supplies. An energy utility company owning a diversified portfolio of both gas and nuclear generation theoretically has the best of both worlds – selling reliable baseload electricity to consumers from its nuclear generating fleet along with the flexibility to meet peaks in energy demand from its gas-fired generating plant. As a corporate strategy, a gas-nuclear mix is a two-way hedge for a utility company. Nuclear generation acts as a hedge against high gas prices and carbon emission penalties, while gas generation acts as a hedge against high capital interest rate payments for nuclear plants.

The case for new nuclear build in Britain is a complex mix of investment economics, climatic politics and geopolitical security, requiring investors to make many judgements about the coming decades ahead. But at the end of the day, what the political arguments over Britain's future energy technologies really boil down to is a simple choice between the lesser of two evils: whether it is safer, easier, cheaper and more sustainable to deal with radioactive waste from nuclear power stations or carbon dioxide waste from fossil-fuelled power stations; and whether the fuels can be sourced internationally without holding Britain to economic and political ransom by unfriendly foreign governments. If natural gas and carbon prices stay high in the future and a national site for a deep nuclear waste repository can be found, then nuclear power would be a good option for investors and governments alike.

Further Reading

D Victor and D Cullenward, *Making Carbon Markets Work*, Scientific American, 2007.

A Gore, *An Inconvenient Truth: The Crisis of Global Warming*, Bloomsbury, 2007.

J Lovelock, *The Revenge of Gaia: Why the Earth is Fighting Back – and How We Can Still Save Humanity*, Penguin, 2006.

M Klare, *Blood and Oil: How America's Thirst for Petrol is Killing Us*, Penguin, 2004.

C Christenson, *The Innovator's Dilemma: When New Technologies Cause Great Firms to Fail*, Harvard Business School Press, 1997.

B Cohen, *The Nuclear Energy Option: An Alternative for the 90s*, Plenum Publishing, 1990.

Glossary of Terms

3G
Third generation of wireless mobile telecommunications technologies

9/11
The 11th September 2001 terrorist attack on the United States by al-Qaeda

AGR
Advanced gas-cooled reactor, Britain's second generation of nuclear power stations operated by British Energy

AP1000
A modern third generation Advanced Passive 1,100MWe PWR nuclear reactor design marketed by the Japanese-owned American firm Westinghouse

AWE
Atomic Weapons Establishment, which manufactures nuclear warheads at Aldermaston and Burghfield

AWRE
Atomic Weapons Research Establishment, the predecessor of the AWE

BAU
Business as usual, a business planning scenario in which present day commercial operations and revenue models are assumed to continue more or less unchanged into the future

BERR
Department for Business, Enterprise and Regulatory Reform, the government department responsible for setting trade policy; formerly the Department of Trade and Industry

BETTA
British Electricity Trading and Transmission Arrangements, governing wholesale electricity market trading arrangements in the UK

BNES
British Nuclear Energy Society, a professional body for nuclear specialists; now known as the Nuclear Institute following its merger with the Institution of Nuclear Engineers

BNFL
British Nuclear Fuels plc, a state-owned company that developed commercial applications of nuclear energy, mainly in fuel manufacture and spent fuel reprocessing

BNG
British Nuclear Group, the former decommissioning business subsidiary of BNFL whose workforce has now mostly been transferred into NDA Site Licence Companies

BPEO
Best practicable environmental option

C&M
Care and maintenance, an interim stage before nuclear plant decommissioning begins

CAPEX
Capital expenditure, the amount of money spent on buying new plant and equipment

CBRNE

Chemical, biological, radiological, nuclear or explosives terrorist threats

CCGT

Combined cycle gas turbine, the latest generation of gas-fired power station design containing a gas-fired turbine generator and a steam turbine generator employing steam produced from the gas turbine exhaust heat

CCS

Carbon capture and storage, a proposed technology solution for trapping and storing carbon emissions from industrial pollution sources below ground or under the seabed

CEGB

Central Electricity Generating Board, the former nationalised operator of Britain's power station fleet including the country's nuclear power stations

CEO

Chief Executive Officer, having overall management responsibility for running a company profitably

CHP

Combined heat and power, a microgeneration technology for directly producing hot water and electrical energy within people's own homes

CHRS

Culham Harwell Radwaste Service, the first commercialised radioactive waste management service operated by the UKAEA during the 1990s

COBOL

Combined Business Orientated Language, an early computer programming language for businesses

CoRWM

Committee on Radioactive Waste Management, an independent advisory body with oversight of the government's site selection process for a deep nuclear waste repository

D&D

Decontamination and decommissioning, an American term for nuclear clean-up

Defra

Department for Environment, Food and Rural Affairs, the government department responsible for setting environmental protection policy

DG-COMP

Directorate General Competition, the European Commission's competition and trade regulator

DoE

Department of Energy, within the United States government

DRAWMOPS

Decommissioning and Radioactive Waste Management Operations, an early nuclear clean-up programme run by the UKAEA

DTI

Department of Trade and Industry, the government department responsible for setting trade policy, now renamed BERR

EA

Environment Agency, the environmental regulator in England and Wales

EC

European Commission, the executive arm of the European Parliament

ECX

European Climate Exchange, a stock exchange for firms trading carbon permits under the European Union Emission Trading Scheme

EPA

Environmental Protection Agency, the environmental regulator in the United States

EPR

European Pressurized Water Reactor, a modern third generation 1,600MWe PWR nuclear reactor design marketed by the French firm Areva

EPS2

Encapsulated Product Store 2, a state-of-the-art intermediate-level nuclear waste storage facility recently built at Sellafield

EPS3

Encapsulated Product Store 3, a state-of-the-art intermediate-level nuclear waste storage facility currently under construction at Sellafield

ETS

Emission Trading Scheme, a European carbon trading scheme that operates throughout the 27 member states of the European Union

EU

European Union, a community of 27 member state countries with shared political and economic goals negotiated within the European Parliament

EURATOM

European Atomic Energy Community, a specialist branch of the European Union dealing with regulatory controls on civil nuclear power

FGD

Flue gas desulphurisation, an end-of-pipe abatement technology used to reduce sulphur dioxide emissions to the atmosphere from coal-fired power stations

FOAK

First-of-a-kind plant, usually built as a demonstration facility incurring higher manufacturing costs because it does not yet benefit from the economies of scale associated with building several repeat units of a similar design

FTSE100

Financial Times Stock Exchange, a share price index of Britain's leading 100 most valuable companies whose shares are traded on the London Stock Exchange

FY

Financial year, generally running from April to March of the following year for British companies

GLEEP

Graphite Low Energy Experimental Pile, Britain's first nuclear reactor built at Harwell

GNEP

Global Nuclear Energy Partnership, an American programme intended to help supply countries with fresh fuel for nuclear energy generation and take-back spent fuel in order to prevent the extraction of plutonium for nuclear weapons

GOCO

Government-owned, contractor-operated

GWe

Gigawatt electrical, a unit of power indicating the installed capacity of a power station

HEU
Highly enriched uranium, a type of uranium fuel used mainly for powering research reactors, submarine reactors and some kinds of nuclear weapons

HLW
High-level waste, an extremely hazardous type of radioactive waste derived from spent reactor fuel

HM
Her Majesty the Queen

HSE
Health & Safety Executive, the national safety regulator in the UK

IAEA
International Atomic Energy Agency, the specialist nuclear branch of the United Nations

IC
Intelligent customer capability, a nuclear safety licensing requirement

ILW
Intermediate-level waste, a moderately hazardous type of radioactive waste

IoN
Institute of Nanotechnology, a British charitable organisation involved in promoting scientific research and practical applications of nanotechnology

IP
Intellectual property, unique commercially owned know-how

IPV
Independent private valuations, in auction and game theory the unique perceived value to an individual buyer of acquiring an item for sale in the marketplace

ISO
International Organization for Standardization, the world's largest independent standard-setting organisation

KGB
The former Russian intelligence service

LCBL
Lifecycle baseline, the estimated total cost of decommissioning a nuclear site usually over a period of many years now renamed the 'lifetime plan'

LEU
Low enriched uranium, a type of uranium fuel used by civil nuclear energy utility companies for nuclear power stations

LLW
Low-level waste, a type of low hazard radioactive waste

LLWR
Low Level Waste Repository, Britain's national low-level radioactive waste disposal facility at Drigg in Cumbria

M&O
Management and operation turnkey contract to run a nuclear site

MAC
Marginal abatement cost, the cost of reducing an additional unit of pollution, for example one tonne of carbon dioxide

MELOX
A nuclear fuel manufacturing facility at Marcoule in France that manufactures plutonium-based MOX fuel for nuclear energy utility companies

MFFF

Mixed Oxide Fuel Fabrication Facility, an American MOX production plant intended to convert plutonium from retired nuclear weapons into MOX reactor fuel

MIMAS

Micronised masterblend process, a production technique invented by Belgonucleaire for manufacturing MOX nuclear fuel

MIR

A Russian miniature submarine

MoD

Ministry of Defence

MOX

Mixed oxide fuel, a type of nuclear reactor fuel containing uranium and plutonium blended together that can be used in commercial PWR nuclear power stations

MWe

Megawatt electrical, a unit of power indicating the installed capacity of a power station

NASA

National Aeronautics and Space Administration, the US space agency

NDA

Nuclear Decommissioning Authority, the government body responsible for managing and funding public sector civil nuclear clean-up in Britain

NDS

National Disposal Service, a semi-commercial disposal service operated by the UKAEA in the 1990s for old radioactive sources mainly from hospitals and universities

NEA

Nuclear Energy Agency, the specialist nuclear branch of the Organisation for Economic Co-operation and Development

NETA

New Electricity Trading Arrangements, the previous rules on wholesale electricity market trading arrangements now replaced by BETTA

NGO

Non-governmental organisation, such as Greenpeace or Friends of the Earth

NIA65

Nuclear Installations Act 1965, the UK's nuclear safety licensing legislation

NII

Nuclear Installations Inspectorate, the specialist nuclear safety regulation branch within the HSE

NIREX

Nuclear Industry Radioactive Waste Executive, an executive body formerly responsible for radioactive waste disposal planning now merged within the NDA

NLF

Nuclear Liabilities Fund, a state-backed pension fund for financing the future decommissioning of British Energy's AGR nuclear power station fleet

NOAK

Nth-of-a-kind plant, a replica of an existing facility usually built with lower manufacturing costs gained from the economies of scale associated with building several repeat units of a similar design

NOPAT

Net operating profit after tax, a measure of a company's profitability

NPV

Net present value, a measure of the financial value of future business cashflow transactions calculated as if the investments and payoffs occurred at today's prices

NRPB

National Radiological Protection Board, a nuclear standard-setting body now part of the Health Protection Agency

NSG

National Stakeholder Group, a body which advises the NDA on high-level issues generally from a local public rather than a central government perspective

NuLeAF

Nuclear Legacy Advisory Forum, which advises local authorities on nuclear clean-up issues and coordinates local government inputs to national nuclear policy

OECD

Organisation for Economic Co-operation and Development

OFC

Oxide Fuels Complex, a uranium fuel manufacturing plant at Springfields

Ofgem

Office of Gas and Electricity Markets, the energy market regulator in the UK

OFT

Office of Fair Trading, the consumer and competition market regulator in the UK

OPEC

Organization of the Petroleum Exporting Countries, which coordinates policies and prices for oil production mainly amongst Arab petro-states

OPEX

Operational expenditure, the amount of money spent each year on employing workers and paying business running expenses

PBI

Performance based incentives, incentivised contractual payment milestones paid to nuclear decommissioning contractors

PBO

Parent Body Organisation, a consortium of companies holding a nuclear site management contract with the NDA

PF-AFC

Pulverised fuel advanced supercritical, a state-of-the-art generating technology developed for cleaner coal-fired power stations

POCO

Post operational clean-out, the earliest stage of nuclear plant decommissioning

PRICE

A parametric decommissioning cost estimating system developed by the UKAEA

PWR

Pressurised water reactor, a nuclear reactor design using water within the reactor core as both a coolant and moderator safely contained within a pressure vessel

QC

Queen's Counsel, a senior legal barrister professionally recognised as one of Her Majesty's Counsel learned in the law

QQR

Quinquennial Review, an internal five-yearly periodic review by government departments of their executive agencies such as the UKAEA, EA, HSE, NDA, *etc*

RCEP

Royal Commission on Environmental Pollution

RCF

Rock Characterisation Facility, an underground rock laboratory built as the precursor stage to excavating a deep nuclear waste repository

RSA93

Radioactive Substances Act 1993, the UK's nuclear environmental licensing legislation

RWC

Realistic worst case scenario planning, a business school technique used for estimating the worst credible downsides of planned investments

RWMAC

Radioactive Waste Management Advisory Committee, a former independent policy group which advised Defra on nuclear waste issues, now replaced by CoRWM and RWPG

RWMD

Radioactive Waste Management Directorate, the branch of the NDA responsible for building a deep nuclear waste repository at a future site to be selected by the government

RWPG

Radioactive Waste Policy Group, an inter-departmental group responsible for steering the government's overall policy direction on nuclear waste management

SBR

Short binderless route, an automated production technique used for manufacturing MOX nuclear fuel at SMP

SCK.CEN

Belgian Nuclear Research Centre, for peaceful medical and industrial applications of nuclear energy

SEPA

Scottish Environment Protection Agency, the environmental regulator in Scotland

SLC

Site Licence Company, the company employing the permanent workforce of an NDA nuclear decommissioning site and responsible for its day-to-day management

SMP

Sellafield MOX Plant, a nuclear fuel manufacturing facility at Sellafield that manufactures plutonium-based MOX fuel for nuclear energy utility companies

SMP2

A proposed replacement for SMP intended to safely disposition Britain's own plutonium stockpile as an energy source by converting it into MOX reactor fuel

SNP

Scottish National Party, the current governing political party in Scotland

SoLA

Substances of Low Activity Exemption Order 1986, made under the Radioactive Substances Acts 1960 and 1993

SPRS

Sellafield Product and Residue Store, a storage facility for reprocessed plutonium under construction at Sellafield

SPV
Special Purpose Vehicle company, a private sector consortium forming a PBO company that holds a nuclear site management contract with the NDA

SRP
Society for Radiological Protection, a professional body for health physicists

SRS
Savannah River Site, owned by the Department of Energy in the United States

TACIS
Technical Aid to the Commonwealth of Independent States, a European Union programme for funding high-hazard nuclear clean-up in Eastern Europe

THORP
Thermal Oxide Reprocessing Plant, a commercial spent fuel reprocessing plant at Sellafield

TMI
Three Mile Island, the site of America's worst civil nuclear power station accident that occurred in 1979

TRU
Transuranic waste, an American term for radioactive waste containing plutonium and other man-made radioactive elements beyond uranium

UK
United Kingdom

UKAEA
United Kingdom Atomic Energy Authority, a government body which researched and developed Britain's civil nuclear energy capability from the 1950s through to the 1990s

USA
United States of America

VLLW
Very low-level waste, a weakly hazardous type of radioactive waste

WIPP
Waste Isolation Pilot Plant, an underground military nuclear waste disposal repository built in the United States

WISE
World Information Service on Energy, a non-governmental organisation opposed to nuclear energy

Y2K
Year 2000